LINDA V...

Vaginismus

*Understanding & Overcoming
the Blocks to Intercourse*

ASHGROVE PRESS, BATH

First published in Great Britain by
ASHGROVE PRESS LIMITED
19 Circus Place, Bath, Avon BA1 2PW

First published 1988

British Library Cataloguing in Publication Data

Valins, Linda
    Vaginismus
    1. Vaginismus
    I. Title
    618.1'5   RG269.V/
ISBN 0-906798-89-1

Photoset in 10½/12 pt Palatino by
Ann Buchan (Typesetters), Middlesex
Printed and bound by Billings
Worcester

Acknowledgements

I felt it important to write this book in a format which allows both sufferer and specialist to address the reader directly; therefore, this book could never have been written without the input of many people.

Firstly, for the person who never gave up, even when at times I wanted to: love, appreciation and thank you to my therapist.

Special thanks to Dr Paul Brown who read my very first manuscript and encouraged me to continue, and to Robin Campbell of Ashgrove Press who had the courage and commitment to publish this book.

Thank you to Susie Orbach for helping me to understand the social influences on women's psychology, both through her writing and in person.

I am indebted to Dr Leonard Friedman (U.S.A.) for his pioneering publication *Virgin Wives*, 1962; and above all for his help, encouragement and suggestions regarding my final draft.

I am particularly grateful to the following for giving up many hours of their time, offering highly practical and relevant information based upon many years of experience in the field: Dr Paul Brown, Alison Clegg, Dr Martin Cole, Jill Curtis, Anne Dickson, Dr Katharine Draper, Dr Patricia Gillan, Marianne Granö (Sweden), Lorna Guthrie, Richard Johnson, Barbara Lamb, Dr Anne Mathieson, Dr Kenneth Metson, Susie Orbach, Dr Robin Skynner and Dr Robina Thexton.

My sincere appreciation to the following for their help in many different ways, particularly with my research: Dr Morag Bramley, Dr Willeke Bezemer (The Netherlands), Dr Richard Carvalho (Society of Analytical Psychology), Dr May Duddle, Dr Judy Gilley, Judith Green (Institute of Psychosexual Medicine), Dr Keith Hawton, Dr Michael Heap, Incest Crisis Line, Dr Helen King, Barbara Konecny (Swedish Embassy London), Dr Rosemarie Lincoln, Dr Tom Main, Prof. Dr H. Musaph (The Netherlands), National Association for the Childless, Mary-Jayne Rust (Women's Therapy Centre London), *She* Magazine,

Michael Silverston (Commercial & Legal Information Officer Camden), Dr Robert Smallwood (The Shakespeare Institute), Hester Solomon (British Association of Psychotherapists), Yvonne Thomas, Susan Tuck, Janine Turner and Winvisible.

I would like to especially thank and acknowledge Dr Prudence Tunnadine, Scientific Director, Institute of Psychosexual Medicine, for guiding me to some useful medical contacts.

To my family and friends who gave me the space to share my vaginismus with them, and who offered invaluable love, support and 'phone calls, especially: Benig, Charles, David, Dawn, Deirdre, Elaine S, Elaine W, Gordon, Hazel, Heather, Jane, Jim, Leslie, Martin L, Mary, Michael, Nelson, Pauline, Ruth & Tony.

I am indebted to Martin Valins who not only shared the pain with me, but also had to live with a workaholic-writer. He read every single one of the drafts of the book and was my most constructive critic. I could not have written this without his constant love which has seen me through.

Above all, my greatest debt is to the women who bravely came forward and shared with me what were often extremely painful experiences and memories. With the exception of Jan, they have requested they be given pseudonyms for the purposes of anonymity: thank you Carol, Debbie, Emma, Frances, Helen, Jan, Jean, Sarah & Valerie. THIS BOOK IS FOR YOU.

Contents

THIS BOOK IS LOVINGLY DEDICATED TO
MY PARENTS AND MY THERAPIST

Our sexual lives are not normally shared
with our parents and if not for this book I
might never have told mine. However, I felt
that part of the healing process for me and
for other women lies in writing and in
ending the silence around vaginismus. I
therefore acknowledge and thank my
mother and father, as I know how difficult
it may be for them.

Then the stories of blood-stained bridal sheets
and capsules of red ink bestowed on already
deflowered brides floated back to me. I
wondered how much I would bleed, and lay
down, nursing the towel. It occurred to me
that the blood was my answer. I couldn't
possibly be a virgin any more. I smiled into
the dark. I felt part of a great tradition

From *The Bell Jar* by Sylvia Plath.

Reprinted by kind permission
of Faber & Faber, London.

INTRODUCTION

How this book came to be written

Somehow, even as a child, I had always felt that I would not be able to have sex. This fear did not leave me and was brought into even sharper focus when I began to form relationships with men. It wasn't until my most committed relationship, which led to my marriage, that I summoned up enough courage to seek help.

Being able to have sex easily is taken for granted, and certainly for most of us the act of lovemaking is experienced as a natural, desirable and spontaneous part of life. But to women like me who suffer from vaginismus, this natural act is denied, resulting in non-consummation of our sexual relationships and simultaneously depriving us of the opportunity to conceive children. I do not presuppose that penetration is a prerequisite for a loving sexual relationship, or that 'lovemaking' can properly be defined as penetration. There are many couples who enjoy warm, loving sexual relationships without engaging in intercourse: these may include the gay community as well as those who have physical disabilities. Furthermore, despite society's pressures, no woman should ever be made to feel that she is abnormal if she can't have intercourse, nor should she be forced into a sexual relationship. All of us should be free to find ways of affirming, celebrating and expressing our sexuality without needing to resort to rigid norms or fixed ideas about what sex should mean. We should all have the choice as to how we wish to make love. However, for the woman with vaginismus the choice of penetration is, by the involuntary nature of the condition, not an option.

This book springs from the pain and loneliness I felt both prior to and during seeking help. Having vaginismus made me feel lonely, desperate, unsupported and isolated, as if I, and I alone, had this awful condition which nobody else knew about. They couldn't know about it since it was rarely discussed on the radio and never on TV; it hardly appeared in agony columns; very little was written about it. So, I concluded, if nobody knew about vaginismus, who could possibly help me? In dealing with these feelings, I decided that one way of reaching other sufferers would be to share my experiences with them. In doing so, I hope that others may be given the information, support and guidance which then seemed unavailable to me. I felt further inspired to write when I realised that if I had gone through such despair and misery, then it was quite possible someone else had, too.

It has been difficult and often painful to write openly. So strong are internal and external pressures to make things appear 'nice' and present my story with a smile that many times whilst writing I found myself wanting to protect the reader from the real pain and agony I went through. Although this book is intended to be positive, it must be said that the road to resolution is not always easy, and finding the right therapist may be equally difficult. Often the support and encouragement we may want or expect from friends, family and professionals may not be available. It has been hard sharing my pain with people I know; it has been even harder sharing it in a book. However, the power and strength I have gained from these experiences is within each and every woman who confronts her problem. Knowing this allows me to speak the truth without feeling compelled to protect and reassure the reader, or to suppress the realities about difficulties encountered.

I have been most motivated by the work I have been undertaking with my therapist over a period of more than six years, and which has been the foundation of this book. Therapy has given me the courage to communicate how it feels to have vaginismus, as well as the knowledge that it can be successfully treated.

The aims of this book

This book is partly my story; but I also discuss all the issues surrounding vaginismus as an essentially practical and empathetic guide to any woman who thinks she may have vaginismus. I aim to remove the secrecy and shame surrounding vaginismus and thereby promote greater understanding amongst people in general, as well as amongst medical and sexual practitioners. I hope that this will result in us being able to share any emotional problems freely and more openly. I address you as an individual, respecting your uniqueness. I hope that you will use this book to help you to make your own discoveries which will lead towards resolution. Above all, I want to be supportive, to encourage personal growth, and to assist in the realisation of our potential, our power and our creativity, in order to overcome our problems.

The need for this book

Despite its existence, vaginismus has barely been noticed and has been described as the 'Cinderella' of women's sexual problems.[1] Concentration has been centred on birth control, abortion or choices in childbirth to such a degree that I feel that there is a need to redress the balance. It would be comforting for us to walk into bookstores and see literature on vaginismus in addition to these other issues.

> I'm just so glad that someone is writing a book about this as I feel that we are the forgotten few
> (Valerie)

I highlight the need for vaginismus to be recognised as an essential issue in women's literature. Even more important is the need for a more positive and sensitive appraisal of the sufferer. During my research I have been struck by the innacuracies of some of the descriptions of both the condition and the sufferer. Many of the characterisations seem stereotypical and damaging, reinforcing an already poor self-image. Words such as 'frigid' and 'childish' are not only negative, but they do not paint a true picture of a woman who has vaginismus. The majority of us are warm, loving and sensuous, consciously longing for intercourse but unconsciously fearing it.

Apart from *Virgin Wives* (1962) there have been no books solely about vaginismus. Whilst an excellent and concise study, *Virgin Wives* is almost thirty years old and is primarily a medical text. I was interested to see that the book closes with a plea by its author, Dr Leonard Friedman, urging that as vaginismus has never before been discussed at length it be further researched and more widely understood.

Is this book only for women who have vaginismus?

No. Whilst it's true that this book is about vaginismus, the causes and ways in which help can be sought are similar and equally applicable to *any other emotional problem*. This book will also have relevance and use to anyone who has either experienced or is experiencing difficulties in lovemaking or relating intimately, even though they may not have vaginismus.

This isn't a medical textbook, nor is it a sex manual; it is a personal statement. A simple but fundamental discovery I made is how important it is to *love oneself* and to *feel loved* in order to *make love*.

I hope that when reading this, you will be able to draw comfort from the knowledge that whatever fears, anguish or pain you may be experiencing, I too have shared similar feelings.

LINDA VALINS
LONDON MAY 1988

CHAPTER ONE

Linda

In describing my background I share with you a brief personal history of my family relationships. However, my background was not in itself a direct cause of vaginismus. Instead, it was the way in which my particular psychology interpreted and coped with such events which was the major factor in its onset and development.

* * *

I was born on 2nd August 1951, the eldest of four children and was raised in a moderate, though comfortable, rented terraced house in North London. My mother endured a long and difficult labour having me, and felt so disorientated that she was unable to notice the precise time of day I was born. She described me as a 'beautiful baby who looked like a china doll'. However, I did not sound like one and cried practically non-stop. My mother developed 'milk fever' and was unable to continue to breastfeed, but I could not make the transition from breast to bottle with ease. My father often told me how he wore out a patch in the bedroom carpet from pacing the floor at night trying to get me to sleep. To this day I still have problems falling asleep.

The house I lived in was shared by my mother's parents as well as my mother and father. Although unspoken, there must have been some tension in this arrangement. Conflicts must have increased when I was born due to the unconscious competition on how best to raise me which was probably generated between my mother and grandmother. It must also have been difficult for my parents to freely express both anger and intimacy under the same roof as my grandparents. My parents tell me that as a little girl I was very loving, but extremely emotionally sensitive. At two years old on a trip to the seaside I refused to place my bare feet in the sand and cried with fright until my shoes were put back on. From a very early age I was scared of the water, and to this day cannot swim.

My parents frequently told us how they'd wished their lives had been different. Both had had opportunities to pursue careers in show business, but for various reasons, including the war, had not been able to follow this through. Consequently, they seemed to invest high hopes and expectations in all their children.

One of my earliest memories was at four years old, having to suddenly share my parents because of the arrival of a younger sister: my reaction is summed up by a family photograph taken two days after her birth, where I am looking into the camera with tears in my eyes.

It was the mid 1950s, when pre-school education was neither so available nor so widely accepted as it is today. I therefore spent the first 5½ years of my life solely in my family's company with little outside contact. I was over-protected and, not surprisingly, my first day at school and sudden separation from my mother was very traumatic. I felt shy and awkward with other children, and I recall my reluctance to go to their birthday parties. I would cry and plead with my mother to let me stay with her. The highlight of my primary school days was the prospect of being met by my father at the school gates. To me he seemed the tallest and handsomest of all the fathers, and my heart would leap when he peered through the glass panel of the classroom door to find me.

When I was six my brother was born. At the time of his birth I had measles and was therefore separated from him and my mother until I'd recovered. Looking back, I can see how this must have felt – to be separated from mother when I needed her badly because of my illness.

At home and at school I was always eager to communicate, and my teachers commonly criticised me for being too talkative. They referred to me in end-of-term reports as a 'chatterbox'. Although I enjoyed and excelled in art and English, my maths was always very poor and I had a 'can't do' attitude. I was terrified of anything competitive and consequently disliked, and was bad at, sports. This was in striking contrast with my mother who had not only excelled in swimming when she'd been a schoolgirl, but was also sports captain.

My feelings of exclusion began early, such as the times I stood at the edge of the pool watching my family swim; and on Guy Fawkes night when, too afraid of the loud bangs from fireworks, I remained alone in doors with my face pressed up against the glass, watching the rest of the family enjoy themselves.

If there were any problems either personally or to do with school, I found it difficult to share them since my parents tended to respond by being over-upset and animated. I then would feel compelled to comfort them, trying to reassure them that I wasn't feeling so bad. The most extreme form of trying to protect them was when at five I developed an infection on my nailbed possibly as the result of intense nailbiting. Rather than tell anyone, I stood in an upstairs bedroom and cried silently with the pain. When I could no longer endure it, I finally showed my mother but by this time it was necessary to have the nail removed in hospital. I still recall the humiliation and shame I felt when the doctor and nurses admonished me for biting my nails. I felt as if I was to blame for the agony, as if I had somehow deserved it.

A major trauma followed at nine years old when my grandfather, whom I especially loved and who used to dress me for school, died of lung cancer. My grandmother and mother had nursed him throughout his illness and I remember feeling squeamish and repulsed by the blood and sputum which were in a bowl beside his bed. Although I wanted to mourn my grandfather's death, there was an air of stoicism common to our household which prevented me from being able to cry openly. I had to suppress all this love and sadness.

In general, whilst anger was freely expressed amongst our family, there was little space or encouragement to share other feelings in an open and sensitive environment. I also had very little privacy or physical space, having to share a bedroom with two other siblings. Conversations appeared to be uninhibited in their range of subjects, but in fact little was discussed or heard at a personal level. Mealtimes were often noisy and chaotic, leading me to feel that my needs were not

being individually heard or met. My parents also accused me
of being overdramatic about things, but this may have been
the result of my initially not feeling listened to; or perhaps I
was merely emulating their animated and over excited
responses. I often felt I was operating on a different level to
them intellectually, meaning they were unable to respond to
the kinds of discussions I wanted to have with them.

However, my home was nevertheless very much a warm,
loving and 'open' one, with people frequently popping in and
friends often staying overnight. An important aspect of my
upbringing was the tolerance, acceptance and generosity my
family displayed.

I was very attached to my mother and admired her
cleverness and her beauty. Although I wanted to be closer to
her, I often felt she could not respond and in turn did not
acknowledge her own love and creativity. My father
remained a distant, exciting but mysterious figure, simply
because he was often absent and worked seven days a week in
a textiles factory. This industry was known for its poor
working conditions and intolerable deadlines. I sensed that
he was tense and unhappy with his work, yet appeared
powerless to change his situation. The times we spent in each
other's company my father was invariably exhausted, and he
tells me how I sat quietly at his feet 'allowing' him to nap in
his chair. Afterwards he would praise me for not disturbing
him. Whilst I felt close and loving towards my sisters and
brother, as the eldest I felt somewhat apart from them, often
having to take on a bossy role which I resented and in which
they still see me. Nonetheless, I have observed in comparison
with siblings in other families how close and loyal we all feel
about one another.

Living within an extended family, my grandparents
(particularly my grandmother) were my 'second' parents. The
boundaries between their respective roles were quite blurred
at times in that it wasn't uncommon for me to eat supper with
my parents and then go upstairs and have a second meal with
my grandparents. Within this almost suffocating atmosphere
I sensed how entwined we all were with one another. This
extended to my mother's reliance upon her mother; she
seemed to constantly seek her help and approval. Whilst in
some ways this was, of course, supportive I came to realise

that it was not very healthy.

I sensed my parents felt torn between wanting to break out from the conformity of their generation and to express themselves fully, yet paradoxically needing to appear like everyone else in their close-knit community. In fact, in many ways my parents were quite 'whacky' and un-conservative. I remember when I was 12 coming home from a friend's house to find my parents dancing the Twist to the record player turned up full volume. This was a side of them which rarely surfaced.

The issues which seemed outwardly important to my family, but which conflicted both with my ability to be my true self and with my parents' to be theirs, included:

- conforming socially
- appearing happy to outsiders
- attending family functions even when not wanting to
- doing and saying the right things even when not feeling them
- avoiding looking at inner conflicts
- pleasing others, even if it meant upsetting oneself

If I had to summarise how I felt as a small child it might read something like this:

> I can't do it. . . . No-one understands me. . . . I feel scared . . . I feel so excited . . . I love mum and dad. . . . I'm so shy. . . . It's all my fault. . . . I hate everyone . . . I feel ashamed . . . I feel alone. . . . Am I loved?

Moving from childhood to adolescence . . . When I was 14 my mother gave birth to my youngest sister. I felt a mixture of emotions: ashamed and secretly envious of her pregnancy as well as elated at the thought of a new baby. I tried to conceal my mother's condition from schoolfriends, but when they found out many made fun of me. At the same time my school also underwent dramatic changes and became one of the first in the U.K. to go comprehensive. All my existing teachers left, and I felt abandoned and alienated amongst children who seemed little like myself. Many of them seemed to be ex-Borstal or offenders, and some, as young as 14, were pregnant. There seemed nobody I could trust, and I would often be punched and bullied because of the 'posh' way I spoke. During this time my escape from such misery was to mother my new-born sister. I would often gladly step into my mother's role and try to take care of the baby and my father. In order to protect my parents from the difficulties I was experiencing, I felt compelled to keep my problems to myself.

My periods began late (at 15) and my mother was so anxious she took me to our doctor to see if anything was wrong. There wasn't, but the idea of inserting tampons terrified me. When my periods finally began I told my mother. She reacted in the tradition of Eastern European Jewish custom by briskly patting me on my cheeks, which was meant to bring colour to my face. She then congratulated me. I was totally confused by the slap and the praise. My mother, therefore, greeted my womanhood with an act of violence which made me feel as if I'd done something wrong. This is not to say there is anything deliberately sinister in this custom, but remember how sensitive a little girl I was.

My periods made me feel embarrassed to be an adult and shameful that men might now find me attractive. I felt awkward when my parents complimented me on my growing body, and their remarks felt prurient and intrusive. My mother rarely spoke about sex and only briefly discussed how babies were made, yet this conflicted with the sexual way in which my parents interacted with each other. They appeared to share private innuendos and their sexual life seemed blatant because they'd created a baby in middle-age.

Although considered academically bright by my head-teacher and a candidate for university, at 16 I left school with few qualifications. I finally trained as a secretary.

My training began in the world of TV advertising where there was little sexual inhibition and illicit relationships between staff were not uncommon. This was also the time of the Swinging Sixties, Beatlemania, the permissive society and the Pill. Here again, I felt apart . . . in conflict. Although I wanted boyfriends and had little difficulty getting dates, as soon as a boy sought an intimate relationship with me I became scared and withdrawn.

As explained in the *Introduction*, I always felt I would not be able to have sex. But how, you may wonder, can a child know this? Perhaps this idea originally stemmed from the belief I would never *become a woman* rather than never be able to have sex . . . this probably came later. Even at 18 and 19, I would still be looking on as an outsider at other grown-ups, and this was finally encapsulated in my belief that I could never engage in their most adult of acts.

Throughout my late teens I had a series of boyfriends, but my fear of lovemaking was now so strong that the relationships inevitably ended. In common with many people of my generation I spent a large part of my twenties travelling to different parts of the world, but never escaped the mystery deep inside me. No matter how many people I met or became close to, I never felt able to share this pain. When I returned to London I resumed secretarial work and although I received praise from employers I never felt fulfilled in this role. Most of my friends were in chosen professions but I had the same 'can't do' attitude when they asked why I didn't pursue a professional career. I was 22 when I met my husband-to-be and he was the first person I could tell that I was frightened of intercourse. He listened and didn't laugh or reject me. It was his later support and encouragement which finally led me to seek help.

Today I feel as if I'm more open as a person and, more importantly, I am beginning to know and understand myself. I hope you, the reader, will be able to get a sense of who I am and how I feel from this and the forthcoming chapters.

CHAPTER TWO

What is Vaginismus?

The Clinical Definition

It was by reading books like Dr. Delvin's *The Book of Love* and *Treat Youself to Sex* by Brown & Faulder that I discovered the problem I was suffering from actually had a name: 'vaginismus'. Up until that time no doctor had made this diagnosis. This demonstrates not only how difficult it was for me to seek help, but also how difficult it was for doctors to help me. Jean had almost thirty years of suffering before she was told she had vaginismus:

> Since the 1950s I've had no end of treatments, but it was only last year when I saw a new therapist did anyone tell me what was wrong with me
> (Jean)

Vaginismus is an involuntary spasm of the muscles surrounding the vaginal entrance which occurs whenever an attempt is made to introduce an object, including a penis, into the vagina. Generally the spasm is limited to the vaginal opening, but many women also suffer from spasm of the muscles of the thighs, anus, abdomen and buttocks. Each muscle or group of muscles can come into a state of spasm during attempted or anticipated intercourse.[1] Vaginismus isn't a disease, nor is it a physical disability. It is an emotional condition, the causes of which are psychological but which manifest in a physical response. Consciously we very much want to experience penetration, but deep down we are saying 'no!' The unconscious muscle control of our vagina is able to take over from our conscious mind whenever intercourse is attempted.

Doctors refer to two types of vaginismus. The first

(known as 'primary') is where a woman has never been able to tolerate penetration and the vaginismus has been present in every sexual relationship. The other type (known as 'secondary') is when vaginismus occurs in a woman who has previously enjoyed intercourse and then develops spasm after, say, a trauma. Doctors also differentiate between 'non-selective' vaginismus (when the spasm appears with every partner) and 'selective' (when it appears with a specific partner). Furthermore, vaginismus may sometimes be distinguished from 'apareunia'. This is when a woman is able to insert her fingers or a tampon into her vagina but is unable to have intercourse. However, for the purposes of this book vaginismus and apareunia will mean the same.

There are varying degrees of vaginismus ranging from a mild, occasional spasm to a very severe one:

> Even now you get some of the young Senior House Officers in gynaecology who find it annoying when they're doing postnatals, and here's this woman, she's had two babies and she's still difficult to examine. You get a lot of middle grade vaginismus, not total vaginismus, which causes pain and women get tense, it puts them off sex but it isn't that absolute total barrier that it can be for some women
> (Dr Katharine Draper, Member Inst. of Psychosexual Medicine)

Although vaginismus is commonly referred to as a 'sexual problem' this isn't necessarily the way all therapists define the condition:

> Whether vaginismus is to do with sexuality is not for me a closed issue. There's an assumption that it's about sexuality, but I would be inclined to take a different starting point. It might be more about a woman's emotional receptivity having been damaged in some way because of what's been learned in the very early family history
> (Susie Orbach, Psychotherapist)

Defining vaginismus is by no means a black-and-white issue. Indeed, the term can be used more loosely by doctors than the way in which I've defined it. In this way vaginismus is seen purely as a description of a symptom; neither a condition nor a diagnosis, but rather a way of describing what happens when a doctor tries to examine a woman vaginally. To use the word vaginismus to simply get a woman referred for treatment may not always be appropriate, because in some instances our reluctance about being examined may be perfectly normal and we may just need some reassurance to overcome our difficulty.

OUR PERSONAL DEFINITIONS

> Vaginismus is a medical term for a lot of pain, a lot of suffering and a lot of humiliation
> (Jan)

Medical definitions are not personal definitions. They are purely clinical and do not describe or convey vaginismus in terms of what it means for each of us. For me, vaginismus is 'a total blocking of all possibilities'. That's to say, at its most destructive and powerful the spasm would appear vaginally, preventing me from being penetrated and creating new life. But vaginismus wasn't just confined to my vagina. It also came into operation on other levels. It blocked my relationships with people by preventing me from opening up and trusting; it blocked my creativity, making my artistic abilities and imagination unavailable; it blocked me intellectually, rendering my powers of intellect unavailable and preventing me from pursuing a career.

Vaginismus is a term we can apply to many processes within us, not just vaginally. For Sarah, it meant absolute fear. She likened it to being held back at school: 'it held me back in every aspect of my life' (Sarah). It was as if she continually failed in one vital subject, and no matter how good she was in all the other subjects at school, being hopeless in this one crucial subject prevented her from getting into any job or other areas of her life.

Another sufferer, Jan, defines her vaginismus as 'a closing off and shutting down of myself against the outside world'.

Although vaginismus manifests universally as a vaginal spasm, it nevertheless results from a diverse range of conflicts, the origins of which may range from psychological to social. Each woman's vaginismus, though resulting in the same symptom, will be as unique as the causes that produced the spasm.

IS VAGINISMUS THE ONLY CONDITION WHICH PREVENTS PENETRATION?

No. There may be reasons for non-consummation other than vaginismus, and often the explanation can be simple.

Fear and inexperience

Whilst not actually having muscle spasm, we may be tense and anxious about our first experience of intercourse. Our partner might get to the vaginal entrance, whereupon we might flinch a bit causing him not to push any further for fear of hurting us.

Another simple reason for non-consummation is that often neither partner realises that it can be crucial for one or the other to use their hand to guide the penis into the vagina.

Painful intercourse

'Dyspareunia' is the medical term for painful intercourse. It's important not to confuse this condition with vaginismus because dyspareunia *allows* penetration, albeit painfully. It is usually caused by physical, not emotional, problems. If dyspareunia remains undiagnosed and untreated, the anticipation of pain during penetration induces muscle spasm as a protective reflex.

Even though most infections do not actually involve the vaginal entrance, the fact that an infection can make penetration painful may eventually lead to vaginismus.

I haven't listed them all, but some causes of dyspareunia may be:

- congenital deformity of vagina (including a rigid or impenetrable hymen).
- infections which lead to pelvic inflammatory disease, such as herpes, thrush or vaginitis.[2]

- hormonal abnormalities (menopause or endometriosis).
- trauma (brutal sex, or scarred stitching of perineum ('episiotomy') after childbirth.)
- allergic reactions or hypersensitivity to contraceptives or lover's sperm.
- tumours of the pelvic organs, bladder or rectum.
- insufficient lubrication as the result of inadequate foreplay or poor sexual technique.

If the above are not diagnosed and treated, then over the months or years intercourse can become increasingly painful and may result in vaginismus. Sometimes even after an infection is cured a woman may still associate intercourse with pain. If medical examinations rule out any physical cause for the continuing pain then, like vaginismus, dyspareunia may be considered psychological in origin.

In talking with women who don't have vaginismus, some tell me they dislike penetration because it feels invasive or painful. They confirm that there's nothing physically causing the pain but then go on to reveal how unhappy their relationships are with their partners. This leads me to conclude that painful intercourse may sometimes be a type of vaginismus in that the pain is being sustained psychologically, not physically. Dyspareunia can, therefore, be treated in the same way as vaginismus.

> Sometimes I've had a woman who has said she has difficulty with intercourse and I've examined her quite easily. But while she's been on the examination couch she has suddenly started talking about something that's bothering her, and you can feel the vaginismus develop on your finger. So it can be very variable according to what is actually happening
> (Dr Katherine Draper, Member Inst. of Psychosexual Medicine)

IS VAGINISMUS A SEXUAL PROBLEM?

At first glance vaginismus may appear to be a sexual problem since it clearly affects our ability to use our vaginas sexually. However, the origins of vaginismus don't lie in a woman's vagina or her sexuality. They lie elsewhere in the areas of:

- – fear of intimacy
- – fear of dependency
- – lack of self-love
- – poor self-esteem
- – lack of trust
- – feeling unentitled to needs

The reason why vaginismus is often felt and seen to be a sexual problem and thus mainly treated in a sexual way is simply because it *becomes* a sexual difficulty. However, the reasons why a symptom manifests in our vaginas will be different for each and every sufferer. I therefore place vaginismus in a wider context so that the condition may be viewed outside our preconceptions of its relationship to intercourse, the vagina and the penis.

As psychotherapist Susie Orbach has already explained, whether vaginismus is to do with a woman's sexuality is not a closed issue. It may have far more to do with a woman's emotional not genital receptivity. Sometimes vaginismus dealt with exclusively at a sexual or genital level can be somewhat of a 'red herring', leading both sufferer and therapist into a less effective understanding and resolution. It may, for example, unnecessarily involve examining our partner's sexual potency as well as offering us sexual techniques and vaginal gadgets aimed solely at achieving penetration.

As Dr Willeke Bezemer, a Dutch sexologist, explains in her paper on vaginismus, an enlightened therapist would argue that the outcome of treatment which results in a woman explicitly not wishing penetration is as legitimate and as good a result as a woman's desire for intercourse being satisfied.[3]

When sufferers share what penetration represents and why they feel unable to allow it, their comments indicate the depth of what intercourse means. Frances explains how vaginismus relates to fears about intimacy and her inability to feel loved, not sex itself:

> In sex I give myself and take in the man. To give and

accept everything that oneself and the other person is
seems to me a huge monumental act that's also very
ordinary. I always feel when attempting to make love
that my deepest self is inside me and I'm not at all sure
that who I am is known, loved and accepted
(Frances).

WHEN WAS VAGINISMUS FIRST IDENTIFIED?

An important and comforting discovery for me was the fact
that I didn't personally 'invent' vaginismus: it is a condition
one develops. Therefore, there must always have been
women who suffered from it throughout the ages. After
understanding the ways in which *I* developed spasm I saw
that the causes are not unique either to me or to any other
woman in past or contemporary society. Indeed, vaginismus
can potentially develop in any woman regardless of age,
colour, class or culture. Vaginismus existed in women before
you and I. We are not the first, and we are definitely not alone.

The earliest medical reference can be traced in Quincy's
Lexicon Medicum, London 1802, and in its successor in 1833.
Suggested treatments around this time were always surgical,
because psychotherapy was still an undeveloped field.
Thankfully, recent entries in the medical dictionaries now
concentrate upon the possible psychological nature of
vaginismus and no longer suggest as a method of treatment
such outmoded surgical procedures. Other early references
dating back to 1880 are also found in homoeopathic medical
textbooks. It is a paradox that the more conventional medical
literature affords comparatively little information to vaginismus, whereas 'unorthodox' medicine devotes numerous
pages listing a myriad of remedies.

The term 'vaginismus' apparently originated with a Dr.
Sims, an American gynaecologist during the Civil War.[4] He
was the first to describe the condition at a meeting of the
Obstetrical Society in London in 1861. Further reference is
made to vaginismus by Havelock Ellis (1859–1939), a British
physician specifically interested in researching sex, relating
to a case study in 1896.[5]

However, the greatest contributor to the study of

twentieth-century sexuality was undoubtedly Sigmund Freud (1856–1939). A psychiatrist practising in Vienna, Freud introduced the concept of association between mind (psyche) and body (soma): hence 'psychosomatic'. As a treatment, psychoanalysis has a direct relevance to vaginismus since spasm is psychosomatic, induced by deep-rooted fear and anxiety. Vaginismus clearly demonstrates the unconscious use of our body, and a psychoanalyst would aim to discover the link between the present symptom (spasm) and past experiences. Freud used techniques to reach the unconscious as he believed problems can most effectively be resolved through the exploration and mobilization of early, repressed infantile experiences which give clues to reasons for the present day vaginismus. Reflecting the patriarchal era he lived in, Freud's work focused primarily on male psychology and sexual behaviour. He seemed to profess ignorance about vaginismus, but did discuss the condition with his former pupil and colleague Karl Abraham during correspondence in 1924.[6] Despite the hostility and disgust that some of Freud's theories aroused (notably his discovery of infantile sexuality) the concepts and techniques which he developed still influence the majority of today's therapies, many of which are used to treat vaginismus.

It wasn't until the study of sexuality was popularized in the late 1950s by Masters and Johnson, the renowned American sex researchers, that vaginismus gained more prominence as an identifiable and treatable condition. Masters and Johnson are seen as the pioneers of sexual therapy which, following their radical studies of female sexual response, became a major treatment for vaginismus (more about this and other methods in Chapter Five).

Although vaginismus isn't mentioned by name in literature, it is interesting to note, for example, that Shakespeare's Ophelia is blamed by Hamlet for not consummating their affair.

The novelist Sylvia Plath gives an account in *The Bell Jar* of the heroine, Esther, haemorrhaging during her first traumatic experience of penetration.

How often does the heroine in romantic novels and films whisper to her lover as she is about to be 'taken': 'Darling, be gentle with me'?

Somewhere there is an unspoken, unconscious fear of pain around allowing someone inside us, common to all women, and enough for it to be alluded to in literature.

> I keep wanting to change the ends of novels by putting the women into therapy
> (Dr. Katharine Draper, Member Inst. Psychosexual Medicine)

And we mustn't forget all the childless, royal couples in fairytales who are magically 'presented' with a much longed-for baby. Doesn't this eerily echo some of the psychological conflicts of women who can't have penetration and are desperate for a child? Perhaps the appeal and popularity of myths and legends lies in the way unconscious fantasies related to a developing child are represented in these stories.[7]

Vaginismus is, however, specifically mentioned in one book, *A Crying Game* by Janine Turner. This is the true story of a battered wife who suffers from vaginismus. It is the only book I've come across in non-medical literature which describes both the symptoms and causes of vaginismus within the painful account of a violent marriage.

IS VAGINISMUS RARE?

> No. I would say that in any group of ten doctors there won't be many who won't have encountered vaginismus
> (Dr. Katharine Draper, Member Inst. of Psychosexual Medicine)

One consumer guide on therapies reports that every sex therapist has seen at least one couple whose relationship hasn't been consummated due to vaginismus.[8] This must be quite a few couples!

Although much of the discussion about vaginismus centres around the extreme case where a wife remains a virgin, this may represent only a small proportion of women who experience pain with penetration. One American study cites that many more report having had similar (vaginismic) experiences during periods of stress and marital difficulty.

When viewed in this broader context, vaginismus is a much more common occurrence.[9]

> I tend to see more vaginismus because I do referral clinics. During one year I do approximately 264, that is, approximately five psychosexual clinics per week. I think perhaps 50% of all patients have vaginismus. I also do family planning clinics and meet vaginismus often enough . . . there might be one in a session of twenty women
> (Dr Robina Thexton, Member Inst. Psychosexual Medicine)

A disproportionately small amount of material is published on vaginismus in relation to other female sexual problems. Some books devoted to female sexuality don't even mention the condition! Why is this?

> Perhaps it's easier to write about men's problems as they are discussed in technical terms. Women's problems, like vaginismus, are put in terms of feelings and not just technical happenings
> (Marianne Granö, Sexual Psychotherapist, Sweden)

One reason for the continuing lack of accessible information since *Virgin Wives* might lie in the misconception that vaginismus is a rare condition when, in reality, it's far more common than it appears. Whilst not part of our everyday language, vaginismus has nonetheless generated a whole series of medical papers in countries as diverse as Russia, Bulgaria, Poland, Czechoslovakia, Ireland, Sweden, Denmark, France, Germany, Holland and Australia, as well as in the U.K. and the United States.[10] In addition, a Dutch sexologist gave several lectures on vaginismus at the 8th World Congress of Sexology held in Heidelberg, Germany, in June 1987. Vaginismus is, therefore, a global concern.

Confusion about its rarity seems to arise from a contradiction: some medical texts suggest it is rare, while others say it isn't and that the apparently low incidence is not so much evidence of the low number of sufferers as an indication of the few women who come forward

> Because we can't come forward and say we have

vaginismus it's not thought to be a priority and gets pushed into the background.
(Sarah)

This underlines the dangers of taking statistics at face value.

VAGINISMUS: THE STATISTICS

Statistics, whatever the numbers, can never convey the years of concealed anguish nor intensity of pain and despair that vaginismus causes to each and every one of us. We need to remember this when considering the following:

- Approximately 0.17% of women aged between 15 and 64 (i.e. over 27,200) in the U.K. alone are estimated to suffer from vaginismus.[11]

- There is a higher incidence (0.49%) amongst women aged between 15 and 24. This may represent the period during a woman's life when she first attempts intercourse.[12]

- One study reveals that women of all ages are statistically more at risk from developing vaginismus than they are of having to seek an abortion.[13]

- One doctor specialising in sexual problems estimates that vaginismus occurs in approximately 5 out of every 1,000 marriages in Ireland.[14]

- Another survey reveals that 16 out of every 100 women consulting one family planning clinic were presenting with vaginismus.[15]

- Between April 1986 and April 1987 a leading newspaper's problems page sent out 1,000 leaflets on vaginismus compared with 1,500 leaflets on how to enhance lovemaking.[16]

- Out of the total number of diagnoses made in the sex therapy clinics of National Marriage Guidance Council over a three-year period, approximately 7% of the diagnoses were vaginismus. In the same period approximately 300 cases of pre-orgasmic problems were seen compared to approximately 150–200 cases of vaginismus.

Why then is vaginismus apparently locked into a cycle of misconception about its rarity and low incidence? Part of the reason might be an unwillingness on the part of the sufferer to come forward. Shame and loneliness combined with lack of information and not knowing how to seek help contribute to vaginismus remaining unreported and untreated. When vaginismus remains untreated, statistics will only reveal reported cases.

Vaginismus goes undiagnosed by doctors through inadequate training. One study reveals that a woman had had extensive investigations for infertility before the fact of non-consummation was elicited.[17]

> An increasingly common method of a woman coming for help was that she had been through everything to do with fertility investigations, often for several years, and then somebody had asked her whether she was having intercourse. It's often found out very late on in fertility clinics that the couple are not in fact having intercourse. (Dr Paul Brown, Consulting Clinical Psychologist)

– Women who seek help for vaginismus are often seeking it from various sources and in a variety of places, namely via the general practitioner, family planning clinic, gynaecologist, psychologist, psychiatrist, sex therapist, psychotherapist, psychoanalyst, hypnotherapist or marriage counsellor. With no centralised co-ordinating body collating statistics on vaginismus nationally, this means the statistics available are often fragmented, difficult to interpret or out of date. Because they are largely incomplete, they do not give vaginismus the recognition and prominence it deserves.

– A further impediment to collating statistics is the fact that vaginismus is a variable and not always permanent condition, occurring as it sometimes does following a specific event or untreated infections. Since it can develop in any stage of our lives, the number of sufferers is constantly in a state of flux and, therefore, difficult to assess accurately.

These factors, combined with other issues discussed later in this chapter, all result in the myth that vaginismus is not only rare, but doesn't occur in high enough numbers to warrant serious attention.

> I think doctors have got to take vaginismus pretty seriously. People who say that it isn't a very big problem are just shutting their eyes to it
> (Dr Robina Thexton, Member, Institute of Psychosexual Medicine)

HOW DO YOU KNOW IF YOU HAVE VAGINISMUS?

I am like all women who have vaginismus: anatomically normal and physically no different from any other woman. Whilst unable to have intercourse, we are nonetheless sexually responsive and very much long to make love. Though we fear penetration, we're still capable of sexual arousal and orgasm. Indeed, vaginismic women and their lovers often report a rich and varied sex life.[18]

> There's a myth amongst the general public that there's no sex when a woman has vaginismus. In fact, very many women who have vaginismus are really quite sexual. Not only are they orgasmic when their partner stimulates them, but they also are orgasmic during self-stimulation
> (Alison Clegg, Sex Therapy Training Officer, National Marriage Guidance Council)

Expert confirmation of self-diagnosis

The following isn't meant to teach you how to diagnose your own vaginismus, but rather to help you take the first step towards arranging an initial consultation with a doctor or therapist. Regardless of any suspicion either you or a therapist may have, an accurate diagnosis of vaginismus can't be established without the specific evidence gained from a pelvic examination. Even if an internal isn't possible, an intuitive doctor should still be able to diagnose vaginismus from sensitive observation of the patient's behaviour on the examination couch or inability to tolerate an internal. Without this consultation, women risk being treated for vaginismus when spasm is not present or, conversely, there may be a delay in the correct diagnosis because the existence of vaginismus has not been suspected by a therapist.[19]

A firm diagnosis of vaginismus is not just for the woman's benefit, (she is often relieved that there is nothing physically wrong with her vagina) but it is also important for the therapist:

> I don't like to start work with a woman unless a physical condition has first been eliminated. A clinical diagnosis which confirms there is no pathology therefore gives me absolute confidence to encourage and enthuse the client that we both can do it
> (Alison Clegg, Sex Therapy Training Officer, National Marriage Guidance Council)

1. Physical clues:

Vaginismus manifests itself physically in a number of ways and perhaps you will be able to identify with one or more of these symptoms. Of course, you may have your own which are not included here:

- The muscles surrounding the vagina contract involuntarily and go into spasm if intercourse is anticipated or attempted.

- These same muscles contract making it impossible to insert a tampon or allow an internal examination.

- If an attempt is made either to penetrate or examine the vagina, the muscles of the thighs, anus, abdomen and buttocks draw together. To escape the doctor's approach we may arch our backs and withdraw towards the head of the examination couch.

Carol gives a graphic description of what happens
physically when she tries to allow penetration:

> I was completely tense and he tried to enter me. The
> pain was incredible, that's the only word I can think of
> . . . it was like I was being ripped open and sandpaper
> was being used on me. Afterwards I cried uncontroll-
> ably
> (Carol)

2. *Psychological clues:*

Other early indications, whilst not manifesting physically,
can be described as fantasies, fears and feelings. These may
emerge long before penetration is attempted and often
remain deeply inside us; we may find it difficult to express
them clearly in words. Any one of the following *combined
with involuntary spasm* might be an early indication that
vaginismus is present.

Fantasies play a large part in the onset of vaginismus and
you may recognise your own amongst the following,
commonly expressed by sufferers:

- fear and anxiety that the penis is too large for the
  vagina.

- belief that vagina lacks elasticity, is too small and
  tight, and therefore won't stretch to accommodate an
  erect penis.

> As a teenager I was so thin, I assumed my vagina must
> also be too small and tight
> (Sarah)

- Penetration is associated with pain and damage,
  imagining we'll be ripped or torn apart if entered.
  Because of this phobia, sexual contact which might
  lead to intercourse is often avoided.

- acute anxiety about all the body's orifices, and a fear of touching our insides:

> There are women who are frightened of any kind of penetration. One woman couldn't bear anybody looking at or touching her umbilicus. Others say they can't bear dental treatment either.
> (Dr Robina Thexton, Member Inst. of Psychosexual Medicine)

– strong negative feelings including revulsion towards the vagina and being afraid to look at it or touch it. This can compound our ignorance about where the vaginal opening is actually located.

– one distinguishing trait is that we imagine ourselves to be 'cloacal': that is, possessing only one orifice through which we urinate, defecate and make love.

– irrational fears about our bodies which bear no relationship to fact and are not necessarily connected with inadequate sexual education: for example, fear that the penis will penetrate the abdominal wall and damage internal organs; imagining the vagina to be a bottomless pit that will 'swallow' things up; confusing vagina with rectum, imagining a tampon or penis will go into the back passage by mistake:

> One woman showed me that when she examined herself she could never find her vagina and I observed that her finger always slipped further behind. Then, during hypnosis, we were able to make the link that a man who had assaulted her when she was four had put his finger into her anus, and that had fixed her sexuality
> (Dr Anne Mathieson, Medical Hypnotherapist)

– Fantasies about the hymen are common, too. This may be the result of partial intercourse when the partner manages to penetrate a little but suddenly the vagina goes into spasm and prevents any further penetration. The woman then believes the penis is being blocked by an 'inner' hymen which is high up inside. Other fears are that the hymen is still intact or so strong it has to be removed surgically before intercourse.

3. Historical clues:

Many women have had a horrifying penetrative experience of another sort, such as a rectal biopsy or passing of a catheter into the bladder
(Dr Robina Thexton, Member Inst. of Psychosexual Medicine)

- initial painful or clumsy attempts at penetration
- aftermath of sexual abuse or rape
- traumatic pelvic/rectal examination
- expectation of painful intercourse because enemas or soap suppositories were administered in childhood which caused pelvic pain

ARE WOMEN WHO HAVE VAGINISMUS ALL ALIKE?

There is no true picture of a woman who has vaginismus
. . . all are different
(Barbara Lamb, Nurse Psychosexual Counsellor)

Although we share the same symptom, we have to remember that each and every one of us is unique.

With vaginismus, one is bracketing together events which have different causes, but are simply identified by the same symptom
(Dr Martin Cole, Sex Therapist)

The majority of doctors and therapists agree it is very important not to give sufferers more labels by saying they are in a particular state for a particular reason. One therapist pointed out that the symbol of a woman's spasm is actually very individual and will have a private meaning for each woman.

However, there is perhaps just one common factor:

> The sufferers are very different from each other. Of course, I work all the time with the father-mother relationship in mind, but that's the only similarity (Marianne Granö, Sexual Psychotherapist, Sweden)

THE CONSPIRACY OF SILENCE

How can a condition so serious and potentially widespread remain comparatively unspoken and unwritten about? This, too, in a society which seemingly promotes sexual freedom in the media as often as our favourite recipes?

Or are we so sexually free? Sex still remains an emotionally-charged area for most of us, so it's easy to see why the very nature of vaginismus makes it difficult to speak about. Talking about it means not only having to describe an intimate act normally experienced and shared just with one's lover, but also having to admit to its failure. Yet it's somehow more than that. It's almost a conspiracy of silence because the difficulty in speaking about vaginismus is twofold . . . the silence is not only maintained by the sufferer but also by those around her.

How sex is seen

- Generally we are unable to speak honestly about sex, having to conceal inadequacy by bravado. So long as we attach shame to sexual problems or believe them and their sufferers to be rare, there can be no space in which little-known problems like vaginismus can be discussed. Denying that sex is commonly problematic inevitably leads to failure to speak honestly about it.

- Lack of respect for and honesty in talking about sex can make it impossible for families to communicate in a comfortable and natural way. This means that parents are often the last people with whom daughters feel they can share their vaginismus.

- The essence of sexual expression is often lost under the deluge of information with which we are inundated. With numerous books and radio phone-ins covering orgasm and obsessed with performance, positions, frequency, technique etc., sex is rarely spoken about except in these terms.

- Heterosexual lovemaking is defined by penetration. This is demonstrated by the fact that a marriage may be legally ended if consummation hasn't taken place. Consequently, we feel vulnerable to exposure and ridicule if we share our vaginismus publicly.

The mythology of the Sexual Revolution

Susie Orbach explains that she believes vaginismus might have been more common in the 1950s. When the so-called 'sexual liberation' of the sixties came into being, which pretended to focus on sexuality but in fact focused on *male* sexual liberation, it then became inappropriate for women to admit to having sexual problems. In the late 1960s and early 1970s when the focus moved to the clitoris it removed the whole emphasis from women who might have needed to talk about vaginismus because the vagina was no longer central:

> Because the clitoris became the major sexual organ, so conversation around penetration moved to the background. This meant that the focus moved to other issues of women's sexuality. With the focus removed from intercourse it then became somehow shameful for women who had vaginismus to even speak up and share their problem
> (Susie Orbach, Psychotherapist)

The potential power of women in the world

Anne Dickson (Sexuality/assertiveness trainer & author) suggests very perceptively one of the reasons why vaginismus may be seen through the 'collective male unconscious' as a symbol of power over men.

I was reminded of the Ancient Greek tale in which the women choose to withhold their conjugal obligations from their husbands until the men stop fighting in wars:

> Vaginismus is an uneasy reminder that women can say 'No'. A lot of men feel extremely uncomfortable about the power of the vagina. It's to do with their unease and discomfort about the potential ability of women to refuse. If we did exert this power in the outside world then the world might change, but we can't, so it remains an undercurrent
> (Anne Dickson)

Doctors' unease about vaginismus

The silence may also be maintained by the unconscious reluctance felt by some doctors to recognise the existence of spasm. Having to treat vaginismus may, for example, require a person to confront those parts of himself which are closed to love and openness. All of us, naturally, wish to avoid looking at these aspects of ourselves. Such unease may take the form of either unconsciously colluding with the woman to deny her problem (by sending her away with no treatment), or of considering vaginismus as purely physical. If doctors shout at us or send us away, then perhaps they need to ask themselves what it is that so terrifies them about vaginismus that they have to do this. I feel it could be the terror of their own closedness, or perhaps envy of the woman who is able to make some kind of protest.

Negative Feelings

- Further barriers to seeking help are fear of ridicule and loss of self-respect, created in part by the belief that having a sexual problem is admitting to failure.

- Owning up to being in a non-consummated marriage carries with it the fear, stigma and shame of being seen by society as part of an improper or even unwholesome union.

– We feel compelled to conceal vaginismus lest we're seen as 'abnormal', partly because of our erroneous assumption that people who have sexual problems are somehow peculiar, in the minority, or can even be picked out in a crowd:

I was afraid everyone would laugh if they knew and I would never be able to face them again . . . it would be so humiliating
(Sarah)

People seem to be frightened of catching vaginismus . . . like a disease
(Jan)

The truth is there are very few people who go through life without ever experiencing a sexual difficulty. We only have to think of the man, worse for drink or under stress, who can't get an erection . . . or the woman who experiences pain during intercourse after an infection, childbirth or marital conflict.

– Because 'cause' and 'blame' are mistakenly so interconnected, we feel somehow to blame for failing in the deepest expression of physical love.

I still feel so guilty that for the first four years of my marriage I couldn't be more of a wife as we never made love properly
(Sarah)

– The shame attached to vaginismus can make us feel alienated from all sexual activity, inadequate and fraudulent:

One woman told me for years she used to sit on the train and look at women around her and feel different and wonder why she couldn't be like the others
(Barbara Lamb, Nurse Psychosexual Counsellor)

I remember before therapy desperately wanting to share

my problem with the first available stranger (be it in a bus queue or on a railway platform). Though it does seem irrational now, at that time the only person I could ever envisage sharing my 'secret' was a total stranger ... someone anonymous who I'd never have to see again. Because I so loathed my vaginismus I imagined everyone else would, too.

VAGINISMUS AND YOUR PARTNER

> Vaginismus puts a great strain and distress on a relationship. A woman is battling with negative feelings about herself and a feeling of lack of success in life which are always counter-productive to happiness
> (Dr Robina Thexton, Member Inst. of Psychosexual Medicine)

Having vaginismus affects all our relationships, but most of all it affects our relationships with our lovers. The effects can be extensive and far-reaching since the severity of vaginismus results in non-consummation of sexual relationships and marriages.

Feeling guilty

> I'm eaten up with guilt about making my husband live a life without sex
> (Valerie)

My husband and I are fortunate to enjoy a close, loving relationship and are able to share many things together. However, despite this, my inability to express my love for him in a physical way eventually led to feelings of my wanting to be free of him and the marriage. I saw this as a way of being free from the pressure to resolve vaginismus. Since we could not engage in penetration we couldn't make babies, I would plead with him to meet someone else and divorce me, thereby releasing me from the guilt I felt at not being able to give him a child.

Ban on lovemaking

> We don't make love, but it's more than that because
> we don't come together sexually at all
> (Jan)

Though it might seem too obvious to mention, the physical
relationship between us also suffered. It's still possible for
a couple to maintain a good sexual relationship despite
vaginismus, and for many years we did. However, as time
passed by and the spasm continued, our whole sexual life
focused on penetration. At this point, sexuality and
making love for the purpose of communicating are lost. I
felt that unless I was penetrated then any sexual contact
was meaningless. Each time I set myself up for success . . .
only to feel a complete failure again.

As one sufferer points out, the mere expectation of the
vaginismus is enough to set the reflex into motion:

> If vaginismus happens once, you feel that it will
> definitely happen the next time, and the next.
> Consequently, it does
> (Carol)

I finally concluded that *no* lovemaking had to be more
preferable to continual failures or sex without intercourse,
and thereafter for long periods I imposed a state of misery
on our marriage: celibacy.

> It was almost like there was a deadly secret between
> us, and after a while we stopped trying to make love
> and never mentioned it
> (Sarah)

> My husband accepts the situation and we don't make
> any attempts at intercourse any more
> (Valerie)

Enforced infidelity

Feelings of guilt and inadequacy washed over me like
waves because I was unable to have complete sex or to
conceive a child. I would then beg my husband to leave me

for a woman who could manage to do both. In effect I tried
to push him into having affairs.

Although the spasm had been present in previous
relationships and prior to this I'd never been able to insert
tampons, nevertheless I fantasised that perhaps my
vaginismus was continuing because I was with the 'wrong'
man. I then imagined taking a lover to 'test' whether I still
would have muscle spasm with him. Although I was able
to work through this fantasy without acting upon it, I can
certainly understand why Jean felt compelled to:

> I tried having lovers, thinking it might just be the
> combination of my husband and me that stopped me
> ... but it was the same. Both men said how very
> relaxed, responsive and sexy I was ... but for all my
> responsiveness I still couldn't make love.
> (Jean)

Threat of marital breakdown

> Vaginismus caused the break-up of my first marriage
> as it broke down all communication between my
> husband and I
> (Sarah)

During the times when I felt at my most wretched, hopeless
and destructive, I wanted to end my life. I then became
unreachable and unconsolable, even to my husband.
Needless to say, the consequence of this was a deteriora-
tion in our relationship, and my partner and I found
ourselves in the midst of a marital crisis which compounded the severity of my vaginismus even further.

Masters and Johnson report that vaginismus can affect a
man's sexual performance and that he may be unable to
maintain an erection because of repeated failures at
penetration.[20] Kaplan also reports that reflecting the
cross-section of relationships generally, the quality of
vaginismic marriages varies considerably ranging from
excellent to deeply troubled.[21]

> However many couples we are talking about, there
> will be as many different effects
> (Jill Curtis, Psychotherapist).

In the light of my own experiences and those of other sufferers, I would like to add that vaginismus places an extreme emotional and physical strain upon *any* relationship, whatever the quality.

CAN YOU INHERIT VAGINISMUS?

> Women frequently say that their mother had this problem. She might say that her mother couldn't make love for quite a long time, 'so I'm just the same as she was'. She is almost accepting permission to have a problem so as not to be better than mother.
> (Dr. Robina Thexton, Member, Institute of Psychosexual Medicine)

I am the eldest of four, and neither of my two sisters has vaginismus. Vaginismus can't be genetically passed down between parent and daughter simply because it is a condition one develops, not one we are born with. Nevertheless, it is possible for a mother with unresolved sexual anxieties to unconsciously transmit feelings to her daughter which can be a contributory factor in its onset and development.

> Women frequently say their mother doesn't enjoy sex. I've certainly had women say 'my sister had to have an operation before she could have sex'.
> I was examining one girl who had vaginismus. She suddenly said to me on the couch 'My mother had a lot of problems with sex, but then she had a dream and she dreamt that Saint-somebody-or-other was doing what you're doing now, and after that it was all right'(Dr. Katharine Draper, Member, Institute of Psychosexual Medicine)

In one case study it was reported that a vaginismic woman recalled her own mother also had the condition, and had difficulty tolerating full penetration to that present day.[22] It would be safe to assume, therefore, that this daughter had psychologically inherited her mother's vaginismus in the same way a very sensitive child might psychologically inherit her father's phobia of thunderstorms.

Though women haven't said their mothers or sisters have vaginismus, some mothers of vaginismic women seem to set up a model for psychological vaginismus in their daughters. One woman's mother would never confront any of the males in the family and would actually go out in the garden to get away from them if there was any trouble. In this case, the mother was setting up in a psychological way exactly what the sufferer is now doing in a physical way.
(Jill Curtis, Psychotherapist)

My therapy revealed that it is more to do with one's emotional perception of mother's anxieties and the way she transmits them rather than any flaw in mother's character, attitude and personality. Any anxieties and attitudes communicated to us by our parents are totally unconscious, and this knowledge helped me to recognise that my parents did not knowingly cause my vaginismus.

CAN A BABY BE CONCEIVED BY A WOMAN WITH VAGINISMUS?

Yes. In some instances vaginismus is only detected in the antenatal clinic or after delivery and spasm is found not to improve after the birth of a child.[23]

Vaginismus and infertility

I saw myself as 'infertile' but felt a cheat for not revealing the true reason for my childlessness. I was hard on myself because, as I discovered in therapy, I felt unentitled to and undeserving of sympathy and comfort. The fact I felt I had to deny I was 'truly' infertile only added to my isolation.

Medically, anyone who hasn't conceived in a certain amount of time is infertile, so we shouldn't isolate ourselves from what could be real support, even if the treatments are inappropriate. Every infertile woman's problem is painful to them and everyone, to some extent, feels a 'cheat' and a social stigma
(Emma)

Unless there are gynaecological problems it can be

assumed that the only relation vaginismus has to infertility is that it can prevent conception. Much of the anguish which surrounded my inability to conceive also stemmed from childhood feelings about an inability to be part of the adult, fertile world and bear my own children. Whilst in one sense a woman with vaginismus is infertile, in another she is not.

Vaginismus and the Law

Interestingly, legal history charts the case in 1926 of Christabel Lady Ampthill, the wife of the Third Baron Ampthill, who gave birth to a son, but not as the result of sexual intercourse.[24] It wasn't immaculate conception either, but rather the baby was conceived without penetration. Lady Ampthill admitted that she was a virgin and that no normal sexual intercourse ever took place throughout her marriage. Records confirm: '(Christabel) admitted that her husband had never effected penetration and that he had been in use to lie between her legs with the male organ in more or less proximity to the orifice of the vagina and to proceed to emission . . .' There is even a legal term for such intercourse called 'conception by *fecundatio ad extra*'. Doctors call it 'intracrural intercourse' where the partner ejaculates on the outside of the vagina. The Law Lords recognised that a child can be conceived without penetration taking place and they ruled in favour of Lady Ampthill. The case resulted in the peerage rights being granted to Christabel's son.

Impregnating oneself

> I think the request for AIH is made quite often by women who desperately want a pregnancy and aren't able to have intercourse in the usual way
> (Dr Robina Thexton, Member, Inst. Psychosexual Medicine)

The wish to become pregnant is understandable; it is a natural longing for many women. For the woman with vaginismus, the desire for a baby is sometimes so overwhelming it can override the wish to accomplish intercourse.

> When I didn't think I was going to get over my vaginismus, and I wanted a child, I thought of asking for artificial insemination but it never got any further
> (Sarah)

Another sufferer describes the longing to fill her internal void:

> I had to know that I was a real woman, that I wasn't frigid. I had to have a child so that I could be fulfilled, yet I couldn't have penetration
> (Jan)

The longing for a baby is sometimes acted upon with impregnation taking the form of one of three procedures:

- The partner ejaculates on the outside of the vagina (as in the Ampthill Peerage case).

- A woman impregnates herself by injecting her partner's semen into her vagina with a syringe (not possible in the majority of women whose spasm is severe)

- A doctor injects semen into the woman by the AIH method (Artificial Insemination Husband).

Delayed labour and traumatic delivery

Dr Draper stressed to me she felt it particularly important that women who conceive despite their vaginismus should have treatment during pregnancy, otherwise the symptom will make the necessary examinations during delivery traumatic and may lead to a delayed labour.

> We had some women in our study who conceived through intracrural intercourse, and they hate the examinations. I think these women are the most urgent to be treated
> (Dr Katharine Draper, Institute Psychosexual Medicine)

Another doctor explains how she uses hypnosis to help the woman who has vaginismus through a subsequent labour:

> I always say to a woman who comes to me with vaginismus that I'd like to see her when she becomes pregnant because pregnant women are particularly responsive to hypnosis. Suggestions can then be made concerning the confidence and relaxation needed for a good experience of pregnancy and childbirth and of successful breast feeding if this is her wish. During pregnancy suggestions can also be made that she will be able to relax and have the confidence to enjoy and express her sexuality fully when she feels ready for this after the birth of her child
> (Dr Anne Mathieson, Medical Hypnotherapist)

It has also been reported that vaginismus is frequently unaffected by the passage of a baby's head during delivery and that women with vaginismus who become pregnant find their spasms much more difficult to resolve once the driving force has been removed.[25]

Is AIH the answer?

There appear to be differing opinions on the appropriateness of AIH for a woman who is not able to resolve her vaginismus. Ultimately, the decision to have artificial insemination will belong to the couple and their therapist. Many therapists told me they would not stand in the way of a woman's free choice to have a baby, despite the spasm:

> If one felt this was a couple wanting a child and they'd approached treatment as honestly as they could, then I would support them in AIH
> (Dr Paul Brown, Consulting Clinical Psychologist)

One Nurse-Therapist told me she felt particularly sensitive to a woman's desperation for a baby:

> I think it would be terribly cruel not to help her have a baby simply because she can't come to terms with her vaginismus
> (Barbara Lamb, Nurse Psychosexual Counsellor)

However, one sex therapist, whilst supporting AIH, is unsure about the long-term effects:

> I think AIH is a good idea, but I have some doubts as to whether a pregnancy helps the vaginismus
> (Dr. Martin Cole, Sex Therapist).

The majority of practitioners told me that generally they would try to play for time and see if they couldn't get intercourse going in the usual way, but they would not rule out AIH.

Often one of the reasons that prompts a woman to seek help is her longing for a child. In the Marriage Guidance sex therapy programme, the wish for a baby is discussed at the outset of treatment:

> One of the terms of our contract is that the clients should use adequate contraception during treatment. I spend quite a bit of time clarifying this since clients with vaginismus often have come for help because they want a baby. It's extremely important they understand that starting a family before the sexual difficulty is properly resolved will almost certainly mean that the sexual relationship will continue to cause problems after the birth of the child
> (Alison Clegg, Sex Therapy Training Officer, National Marriage Guidance Council)

By-passing a woman's subconscious to act on a fantasy

Any concern I feel regarding AIH for a woman with vaginismus springs from my own pain and experiences and hasn't been influenced by doctors or books. I explain therefore why I feel artificial insemination would not have been appropriate for me, so that you may be aware of the possible negative aspects of what may at first seem a short-cut to becoming a mother or to happiness. The practitioners who were opposed to AIH took this view simply because they were concerned for the woman's long term welfare and not because of moral or ethical issues:

As two practitioners explain:

The request for AIH isn't made very often, but on the
whole I would personally be very reluctant because of
the by-passing of psychological difficulties
(Dr Katharine Draper, Member Inst. Psychosexual
Medicine)

I would be very worried about a request for AIH and
my response would have to be 'Hold still a moment'.
For me, it would mean that we've still got a lot of work
to do
(Jill Curtis, Psychotherapist)

Unconscious childhood fantasies which remain active in a
woman's mind may be the real determinants of her wish
for AIH.[26] If we take just one example: psychoanalysis of
children confirms that a girl's discovery that she has no
penis ('penis envy') can feel so depriving that she may deal
with this by denying the differences between men and
women.

In using her own syringe to inseminate herself (as on
page 39), a woman with vaginismus may be acting on an
unconscious fantasy that there *is* no difference between
men and women, and she can therefore make herself
pregnant without a man.[27]

During periods of utter despair and hopelessness, when
I felt that my therapy would never help me, and when my
longings for a baby overwhelmed me, I begged my analyst
to arrange AIH or at least support me in this procedure.

At first, his refusal to help me arrange AIH seemed
withholding and cruel, and I threatened to end my
analysis. However, in being able to understand and work
through these feelings I realised that his refusal to arrange
artificial insemination was actually a loving act and not an
unkindly one. We were able to explore the unconscious
fantasies behind my wish for AIH, and saw that it was
based less upon reality and more on the primitive fantasy
that intercourse isn't necessary to produce a baby. My wish
for AIH was an expression of 'magically' being impre-
gnated, and a natural desire to turn away from looking at
the internal forces within, which produced my spasm.

Again, psychoanalysis confirms that in order to deny the
conflict-laden idea that parents have sex, children often

imagine that something 'magical' is done to mother by a doctor to make her pregnant.[28] If my analyst had supported me in AIH he would have been colluding with me in acting out my unconscious fantasies. We both then would have taken my fantasy about not needing sex to produce a baby quite literally, and he would have unwittingly helped me to by-pass my real problems.

In looking at my own psychological development, I notice that common to women with vaginismus is a strong attachment and inability to separate psychologically from mother. If we don't experience ourselves as being separate from her, then a request for AIH may be an unconscious attempt to get a baby from her.[29] This particular fantasy was very alive inside me; many times I imagined that if I told my mother about my problem she could magically present me with a baby and 'make it all better'.

Echoing my own fantasies, Marianne Granö is careful to notice a woman's inability to separate from mother:

> If a woman's wish to tell mother about the vaginismus is very strong, I always ask why. It may be the fantasy for mother to help her with everything, so it's important to discuss it because we have to recognise how unrealistic it is when you're adult to talk with mother about everything
> (Marianne Granö, Sexual Psychotherapist, Sweden)

In trying to uncover the subconscious fantasies that might lie behind our wish for artificial insemination, I hope not to offend any woman who has conceived a baby other than through intercourse. My concern about AIH is for the woman who suffers from vaginismus, and not for a woman who has physiological problems which prevent her from conceiving in the normal way. Most important, I do not wish to imply that women with unresolved vaginismus can never make good mothers, because of course they can. However, muscle spasm can make future births difficult and there does, of course, exist the possibility that the unresolved conflicts which caused the vaginismus may be unconsciously transmitted to future children.

Our capacity to become good mothers to our children might also be seriously compromised when the forces which drive us are the powerful, unresolved fantasies around 'babies without sex' (i.e. immaculate conceptions and virgin births).[30]

Finally, whilst I've explained the reasons why AIH may not always be appropriate, I do believe a woman should ultimately have the right to choose what she wishes to do with her body.

LIVING WITH VAGINISMUS

The presence of vaginismus can have a devastating effect upon the quality of our lives. Unlike other female sexual problems (for example, lack of orgasm) vaginismus forbids both penetration *and* the ability to conceive, thereby striking at the very core of human creation: our ability to make new life. Vaginismus therefore is unique in that it cruelly combines the misery of a sexual problem with the additional pain and anguish of childlessness.

> Vaginismus has affected my whole life, taken away all my confidence and turned me into a very solitary person. I feel totally inadequate and inferior
> (Valerie)

Loss of femininity and status as a wife

Vaginismus made me feel different from all other women. It placed my femininity in question because being a woman is so deeply connected with making love and making children, neither of which I was able to do.

> I felt a fraud. To others I appeared happily married and seemed to be doing the same things as my friends, but I never felt involved with them
> (Sarah)

I also felt a great lack of control in losing power over two major functions of female life: the ability to use my vagina sexually and my reproductive capacity. Because of my age and the fact I am married, I felt ashamed of my virginity. I was hurting inside all the time but due to the complexity of my emotions I was harsh, self-loathing and unsympathetic with myself.

> We thought of annulment but couldn't face the
> parental anger
> (Jean)

The validity of a heterosexual marriage in society is solely
defined by whether or not it has been sexually consummated. In fact, the law places such importance on
non-consummation that a marriage may be annulled and
any special qualities which might exist in such a union are
seemingly dismissed. In the eyes of society and the law the
virginity of a wife invalidates the legality of her marriage,
making her feel, as I did, that she and her partner are living
a lie:

> I felt a total failure ... I wasn't a whole woman
> because I couldn't have intercourse
> (Sarah)

Exclusion from the sexual and fertile world

Seeing pregnant women and women with children was a
continual reminder of my exclusion from a sexually active
world where women make love with their partners and
bear children together. Sex and pregnancy are ever present
and I couldn't escape the sexual and fertile world, much as I
longed to.

> As each of my friends became pregnant I felt quite
> devastated. I felt envious because their pregnancies
> became proof to me that they had actually done
> something I hadn't
> (Sarah)

Even a commonplace trip to the supermarket or a walk past
Mothercare would produce intense feelings of envy
directed towards the women around me, resulting in a
deep depression. Whilst I felt ashamed of my angry
impulses towards them, this merely reinforced my feelings
of self-loathing. When I was at my lowest my childlessness,
combined with the envy, anger and guilt made me feel that
my only escape from pain would be to end my life.

Being with married friends was also painful. It appeared to me they were constantly talking about contraception or their sex lives and, if that wasn't bad enough, the wives appeared to be forever falling pregnant. This became proof to me of their fertility and lovemaking which my partner and I could not enjoy.

> I think the hardest and loneliest time for me was during my friends' pregnancies. I just wondered where my life was going to lead after that
> (Sarah)

Likewise, maintaining friendships with girlfriends, especially when they were pregnant, became increasingly difficult. I felt tormented by the images I had of their fecund bodies. Because they could have penetration I fantasised that they had 'magical holes' or 'cavernous spaces' where their vaginas were, and I felt a million miles away from them in terms of my physical size and mental growth.

Sadly for some of us, it's not even possible to enjoy friendships with women:

> I don't have girlfriends and don't get on with other women. My therapist thinks this has to do with my feeling inferior because I still feel less than a woman
> (Jan)

No professional help or understanding

Because vaginismus is such an intimate problem it can make us feel we have to resolve it ourselves. Inevitably, this makes it hard for us to even begin to ask for professional help:

> I was far too frightened and embarrassed to go to my GP. He was always so brusque with me and over-worked
> (Sarah)

However, even once professional help is sought, the most appropriate treatment may not always be offered at the first consultation:

> My husband and I went to see about seven doctors

before we finally got to the one who passed me on to the psychologist who actually treated me
(Jan)

The pain of my vaginismus was worsened by the rejecting responses I received from doctors I first contacted. At best they were reassuring but ill informed, telling me to 'just relax, have some alcohol and it will pass'. At worst their responses were cold and indifferent such as 'pull yourself together'. I blamed myself, my demands and my vaginismus for these responses, but it was only as I began to hear other sufferers, who had received identical responses to me, that I learnt to take these remarks less personally:

He told me to go and get drunk, let myself go and I'd be fine
(Valerie)

At his suggestion I tried getting drunk . . . a whole bottle of vodka. I was revoltingly sick with an appalling hangover . . . no use at all
(Jean)

Jean then continues:

They didn't understand me at the Gynae. Clinic either, and said I'd have to pull myself together

The power of healing vaginismus lies within the woman and in her ability to create a healing partnership with the doctor/therapist of her informed choice. In sharing these experiences, I am not accusing all doctors of being intentionally uncaring. However, I've noticed when reading other women's self-help books that the common solution to any problem has been the suggestion that a woman simply seek the help of a GP, doctor or 'expert'. The writers rarely acknowledge or prepare the reader for the fact that it may not be that easy to find someone who is caring, skilled and understanding and who can help you *at the first attempt.*

I saw various doctors, sex therapists and hypnotherapists before I received the appropriate help (Valerie)

> There were only two doctors out of eight who helped
> me. The first gave me a manual which helped me see it
> wasn't just my inability to make love but rather I
> suffered from a definite condition. The second doctor
> referred me on to the clinical psychologist
> (Jan)

Isolation and concealment of truth

> No-one knows about it . . . I'm far too ashamed. I
> know I would have to emigrate if anyone ever found
> out
> (Valerie)

Vaginismus is an invisible handicap. Looking at me you
would never know that I had spasm of the vagina, and
unless I tell people they never know. Because I was unable
to allow my problem to be acknowledged, I didn't feel I was
being authentic. In other words, I wasn't being true to
myself or others. The very nature of vaginismus – the fact
that it manifests in the most intimate part of my body –
made me feel I had to struggle alone and manage for
myself.

The pressure to remain outwardly OK can eventually
become unbearable:

> I seemed to be weeping for weeks on end . . . my
> husband wept too . . . but all the while pretending at
> work and to friends I was having a very torrid sex-life
> (Jean)

Despite its invisibility, we still fear our vaginismus can
somehow be 'sensed' by others:

> It has made my life a very sad and lonely one as I don't
> feel that I can mix . . . I feel that people will guess why
> I'm like I am
> (Valerie)

> I was frightened to open up in any way about myself
> in case people got to my deadly secret
> (Sarah)

Alienation from the family

But perhaps the most difficult pain of all to cope with was the obvious concern (yet insidious pressure) I felt from my and my husband's family because of our childlessness. I wasn't able to explain my vaginismus since I felt ashamed, feared rejection or felt that nobody would understand.

> I didn't once think of telling anyone. Even now that it's all sorted out I still wouldn't . . . I think I would have died rather than tell anyone
> (Sarah)

Our childlessness was 'explained away' as infertility. This led to my being swamped with well-meaning advice from family, friends (and even strangers) about one infertility treatment or another, which was just another terrible reminder of how I wasn't being truthful with the people around me. This led to my feeling further isolated and a belief that nobody knew the real me.

> I think the worst part of having vaginismus is that you can't tell anyone . . . you feel so alone with it. It's not like having a moan to your friends about the sort of problems you can all have a natter about . . . it's a taboo subject
> (Helen)

> I hate to think there are lots of other people living like this. There seems to be a 'club' for most other problems, but this just isn't the sort of problem you can bring up for fear of being made fun of
> (Valerie)

And throughout all my loneliness and isolation I was longing to unburden myself to my mother. But what would she say? How would she react? I felt too embarrassed to make such an intimate confession. Much of the disgust and rejection I feared from her was my own judgmental attitude towards myself: my inability to tell my mother had far more to do with me than with her. As I discovered when I finally told my parents, my fears and fantasies of how they would react to me bore little relation to their actual response. This was one of love and understanding, combined with the plea 'if only you'd told us before . . . we could have helped you'.

However, sometimes the response is not the one we would have hoped for:

> At twenty I tried to tell mum, but she was angry with me and couldn't understand. All the years she'd said 'never let a man touch you there' . . . and I hadn't . . . and when at last it was allowed, I couldn't
> (Jean)

Because of increased media coverage about test-tube babies and surrogacy, people are more aware of the effects of infertility and the plight of such couples. The stress of being childless can be so great that it has reportedly led to divorce and, in some cases, suicide. If childlessness is stressful in itself, imagine the additional stress when it results from, and is combined with, the inability to make love.

CAN VAGINISMUS BE TREATED, AND HOW?

> Vaginismus is distressing but it can be relieved and there's a high chance of success
> (Dr Paul Brown, Consulting Clinical Psychologist)

> Sometimes you can reach success quite quickly. I've had these lovely cases where women are transformed in about two visits. They come back and they look different. Sometimes you can hardly recognise a woman who comes into the room because she suddenly belongs to herself
> (Dr Katharine Draper, Member Inst. of Psychosexual Medicine)

Vaginismus *can* be successfully treated, and often is. However, such success may rely upon our ability to find a sensitive, skilled therapist as well as having the strength and commitment within to engage in such a process.

It is important to state that vaginismus can be treated. Before I sought help, and even at times during therapy, I had a deep conviction it was untreatable.

I never knew that doctors could refer you on to people who could help. I never had the feeling that vaginismus could be treated
(Jan)

The fear that vaginismus is too big and untreatable for anyone originates in infancy at a time when problems and emotions can indeed seem too overwhelming and daunting for a baby to deal with. Again, noticing the connection between today's feelings and my past was a very important step in the healing process for me.

Vaginismus may be treated by a range of methods, most commonly the behavioural and sexual therapies, psychotherapy, or a combination of these. Vaginismus is reported to respond very well, and the prognosis is generally excellent for sufferers. More about these methods in Chapter Five.

To summarize: vaginismus is not rare. Though never fully recognised it has always existed, and once appropriate help is sought the outcome is generally successful.

CHAPTER THREE

What Causes Vaginismus?

Not one particular event or cause

> There are as many different reasons for vaginismus as there are different women. I always see it never being *one* thing that causes anything. It's several factors gradually merging together, and a whole cluster of additional factors that come around that, and then a further cluster of factors around that
> (Jill Curtis, Psychotherapist)

For the majority of us, the causes may be identified with a stage (or stages) in psychological development from which we were unable to move on. If we get stuck at a phase in development this means the necessary growth to take us on to genital maturity may not take place. However, it is rare to be able to trace the causes back to just one particular incident. Usually, nothing specific has taken place, so few of us will be able to blame vaginismus on a particular trauma or event. Not being able to trace one definitive cause of an emotional problem may be the reason why psychotherapy is frequently dismissed as inefficient.

If one specific cause can't be traced it only makes it more frustrating and puzzling for the sufferer, and may be the reason we ask ourselves 'Why have I got vaginismus? How did it happen? Is it my fault? If not, whose?' I have agonized over these questions and I suspect that other women have too. The truth is, it's nobody's fault that we have vaginal spasm:

> Women need to somehow take a compassionate stance toward themselves. This spasm is an attempt to protect themselves from something, but what exactly

we don't know. The way that she is going to change it is to try and understand what it means for her, how it serves her and how she might express whatever conflict it expresses more directly
(Susie Orbach, Psychotherapist)

It is unfortunate that when looking for the causes of problems, all too often we're tempted to fall into the trap of 'Who's to blame?' Blame and culpability have no place when looking at the origins of vaginismus, nor indeed any emotional difficulty. It might be more helpful to begin by asking 'What is the spasm protecting me from?' Asking this can open the doors to understanding how and why we developed vaginismus, rather than attempting to attribute blame to ourselves or to others. It also allows us to make contact with our power, creativity, love and responsibility, all of which are necessary in resolving problems.

Very individual causes

A wide variety of factors may play a role in the causes, as they did in my case, and no single pattern emerges as definitive. Each cause has unique components for each woman which will only become apparent as therapy progresses. What is quite clear is that psychological rather than physical factors play a far greater part in the origins.

> The obvious causes to look for are actual trauma where something unpleasant has happened about the vagina (a learned experience) or where the woman has got cultural conditioning that says sex is bad (an attitudinal experience), or she may have a much deeper unconscious basis connected with her own sexuality as a woman
> (Dr Paul Brown, Consulting Clinical Psychologist)

> There could be a trigger incident at adolescence . . . but the makings of a personality happen very early on
> (Susie Orbach, Psychotherapist)

Many practitioners I spoke with agree that it's very hard to say what causes vaginismus. For example, the issues which often underlie the symptom of vaginismus (fear of intimacy and loss of control, as well as low self esteem) are not exclusive to the woman who suffers from vaginismus. In addition, there is little difference in the histories of those who suffer from vaginismus and those who do not.

Whilst a combination of influences may be common, the mere incidence of one or more occurring does not automatically lead to vaginismus, but suggests other factors may also be involved. Many women with similar backgrounds (sisters from identical environments, or women who experience similar or more severe trauma) do not develop vaginismus:

> Working psychoanalytically, I am trying to put together the pieces in a jigsaw that are so complex for each individual woman. I might even see a patient and think 'Why doesn't she have vaginismus with this kind of history?' but who clearly doesn't. The causes of vaginismus will be so individual, but there are general themes: women's feelings of unentitlement, the fact we're brought up to be terrified of our bodies and sexuality, that our bodies aren't for us, they're for somebody else.
> (Susie Orbach, Psychotherapist)

Our past shapes the present

Even if it's not always intentional, most professions find themselves shrouded in mystery and psychoanalysis is no exception. Yet when we have the opportunity to understand the workings of a profession we're often amazed to see how much of it is based upon common sense. You may be surprised to recognise personal experiences in this section which are similar to mine or those mentioned. You might even think to yourself, 'Oh, so that's why I feel this way . . .' An understanding of our emotional life may trigger greater understanding of the relationship between early psychological development and our vaginismus, and this recognition of the connection between past and present can be a major key to resolution.

Psychological factors tend to fall into three main categories[1]:

(1) DEVELOPMENTAL (by far the most common)
- emotional stress occurring at a sensitive period of development leading to arrestment of psychological growth;

- upbringing invested with guilt, shame and misinformation about sex; strict religious taboos.

(2) TRAUMATIC
- clumsy or brutal first-time sex;
- painful vaginal examinations;
- aftermath of child sexual abuse;
- aftermath of rape.

(3) RELATING TO PEOPLE IN OUR LIVES AND THE ENVIRONMENT ('RELATIONAL')
- inadequate foreplay contributing to lack of arousal;
- fear of being overheard or interrupted during sex;
- partner's impotence or sexual ineptitude;
- negative attitudes and feelings toward a lover;
- conflict and stress in relationship;
- feeling dominated and oppressed by men.

PART I
DEVELOPMENTAL

> To simplify somewhat, I think that in most cases vaginismus is a lack or disturbance of a good relationship with mother
> (Frances)

Incredibly, it was from my infancy* that most of the causes of my vaginismus were identified. Early psychological development is critical and shapes adult behaviour. Some of the origins of vaginismus may be traced to a disturbance in the relating or contact between mother and infant; others to a

---

* A detailed description of the very complex processes relating to early psychological development is beyond the scope of this book. I have therefore attempted to abstract only those aspects which are of special relevance to vaginismus. Included at the back of this book is a personal choice of reading which you may find useful.

reaction a child has to infantile fantasies dating from the first four years of her life.[2] Although the psychological traumas and anxieties inherent in my early growth are part of universal human experience, the effects on me were unique. It's not simply the presence of any event which caused my vaginismus, but rather the ways in which I perceived and experienced these incidents. In fact, many themes outlined here, though specific to vaginismus, are also evident in the origins of other emotional and sexual problems.

Whilst much of the following is based upon psychoanalytic theory, it has not been simply extracted from published information. Instead it is combined with the discoveries I made along the journey I undertook with my therapist: we recreated the baby that I was.

Baby's perceptions rather than real events

Good experiences in infancy can go towards creating healthy emotional development, with consistency in love and care creating a sense of well being within and promoting positive self-image and self-love. My ability to take in good things from my parents and enjoy such feelings depended not only upon real, but also upon perceived events during development. I now realise that frustrating or upsetting experiences in my infancy weren't always caused by inadequate care or attention. As a baby, my hunger, pain and discomfort, even if only for two or three moments, was distressing. My upset didn't necessarily signify my mother's intentional withholding or wilful lack of care, but to be a baby and to feel unhappy with mother or her breast was to be angry with my whole wide world. My mother's presence was felt to be most powerful in my life, and I perceived myself as a helpless recipient of good or bad experiences – a kind of emotional 'puppet on a string'. If mothers have difficulty in connecting with and relating to their babies (because of their own psychology and social conditioning), then the absence of connection may make the process of separation between the two of them less likely.[3]

But how did my anxieties and perceptions become real to me? This relates to my 'unconscious', the contents of which consist mainly of unfinished business and other related matters of childhood, tensions which never become conscious or perhaps once were, and have been repressed. An imagining or fantasy may be just as real to baby's unconscious as an actual experience. Many of my mental images of people or events have little connection with reality, and yet are just as influential on my behaviour as if they were. For example, a 'good' internal image of my mother may have been based upon memories *or fantasies* of what she was like.[4]

Good Mother . . . Bad Mother

Theories developed since Freud suggest that when the person upon whom baby relies for growth and love (usually mother) is unable to relate consistently or satisfactorily to baby's needs, the infant creates a world of internal relationships ('internal object relations') to cope with the disappointments and difficulties she experiences.[5] Called 'introjection' this was when, as a baby, I internalized images of important emotional figures (my parents). Thus, my internalized image of my mother may have had far more to do with my unreal desires and fears about her than the way in which she actually felt or behaved towards me. However, the emotions these fantasies aroused were real. Because my mother was still much needed for my survival, I felt unable to condemn her and consequently took into my developing psychology the idea that it wasn't her responses that were inadequate or inappropriate but rather my selfish, insatiable, devouring, bad (and even loving) needs that were the cause of all my problems.[*] I thus admonished myself and attempted to bury my needs, creating a fantasy world in which badly-experienced aspects of my mother ('bad object') were reconstructed. (See *Linda's Treatment*, Chapter Five). This bad object became split into two images: one part became my teasing, powerful, much-needed mother, and

---

[*] The discovery I made in analysis was the fact that it wasn't simply that my needs made me ashamed, but also that my *love* was destructive. If needs remain unmet and baby feels hateful, she believes her love *and* her hate are the cause of her unhappiness.

the other my rejecting, nasty, hateful mother. The overwhelming presence of persecutory fantasies forced me to develop what is called a 'false self', that is, one which is devoid of needs and shows itself to be undemanding, carefree and contented. My unnurtured 'true self' had been separated and repressed.[6] Sufficiently secure development was consequently thwarted in its progress and the growth required to take me on to the next stage could not be completed. Most of us manage to unknowingly work through these emotions, but it's only when fantasies about my power and destructiveness ('omnipotence') became real to me that problems began to occur.

Psychological separation from parents

Most analysts agree that the root cause of all sexual and emotional problems are unresolved conflicts occurring at specific stages in childhood development. They call all repressed childhood experiences and accompanying emotions 'complexes', the most important one of which is widely recognosed as the 'Oedipus complex'.[7] This was the stage in my development, occurring between the ages of four and five, when I experienced feelings of natural eroticism towards my father.

The potential for a child to break away psychologically from mother and father and enter the adult world in order to seek a sexual partner of her own will depend very much upon the outcome of this. Because the origins of vaginismus are often related to early intense unconscious envy and rivalry toward mother's ability to 'give' father things we can't, the Oedipal stage is of great significance in the development of vaginismus.* (This aspect is further described in *Linda's Treatment*, Chapter Five).

When real events become presecutory and distorted

Psychoanalysis has shown us it's quite normal for a developing girl to have a rich and varied fantasy life

---

* Many analysts after Freud regard the period when baby is totally dependent, not the Oedipal phase, as the stage when psychological problems may occur in development.

depending upon her ability, talents, intelligence etc. Whether a fantasy is cruel, pleasant or sadistic will depend upon the psychological age of a child, and these fantasies seemed to play an important role when I was being analysed.[8]

'Phantasies' are unconscious imaginings, whereas 'fantasies' are conscious. They control our thoughts, emotions and behaviour, as well as the assumptions we make about ourselves. A phantasy may have occurred whereby as a baby I feared injury by a penis to my vagina, leading to expectation of painful intercourse. This phantasy may have been the result of my accidentally witnessing parental lovemaking (called the 'primal scene') resulting in my imagining and distorting activities around me.* Such distorted interpretations of the sexual act or my parents' relationship may have damaged or arrested essential psychological growth. This phantasy produced inner feelings of guilt, envy and unlovability, manifesting themselves in the vaginismus and effectively preventing love and intimacy (including a penis) from entering me later on. (This aspect is also described in *'Linda's Treatment'*, Chapter Five).

Desiring and fearing the penis at the same time

When a girl becomes emotionally more developed, her vagina plays a more important role in her phantasies. She may have magical ideas as to what the penis does to mother's body. Its disappearance during sex and its absence in mother's anatomy then becomes the snatching away of the penis by mother during intercourse. In other words, I may have felt so angry that I had no penis I unconsciously wished to 'castrate' men in revenge for my own castration. This phantasy is called the 'castration complex' which Freud claimed is universal to all girls' development. It is particularly mentioned in psychoanalytic writings as a prototype in explaining vaginismus.

So, for me as a baby the penis was both the desired organ

---

*The 'primal scene' is not only the witnessing of parental intercourse, but also describes when a baby perceives or imagines an exciting, tantalizing but excluding relationship between her parents.

(evoking envy) and the feared organ (evoking anxiety that it would damage my vagina). It was always presumed by analysts in the past that vaginismus is a woman's unconscious wish to snatch away the penis and that unresolved 'penis envy' is likely to result in spasm in later life. However, though practitioners can confirm these concepts it shouldn't be the general rule applied across the board. Clinical experience doesn't confirm the theory that all sufferers have intense penis envy.* One doctor observes that whilst some of us feel angry towards our lovers, just as many don't show signs of hostility and we are relieved and elated when able to have penetration and give pleasure.[10]

Penis envy isn't the only infantile phantasy which can give rise to vaginismus, and indeed not all therapists work within the Freudian framework of such theories:

> I don't see genital relations as an expression of adulthood. I would be looking at what vaginismus means in terms of the 'internal object relations'. That is, how the woman has translated the world of people into an internal world and how that world satisfies or doesn't satisfy her. I don't mean at only a sexual level, but rather how it meets her needs for love and contact (Susie Orbach, Psychotherapist)

It may help to remember that Freud's theories about feminine psychology were developed through the eyes of a man in Victorian society. Therefore, the penis shouldn't be seen simply as a physical organ but also as what it represents symbolically for the baby, ie. how she has translated the world of people into a world of objects such as penis, breast etc. As a symbol of aggression, for example, the penis might stand for the freedom to be, to force one's way, to get what one wants.[11] Viewed in this way, envy of the penis may mean anger and envy of much wider issues, not necessarily related to men. (Discussed further in *Women in Society* page 77)

---

* Orthodox Freudians and writers on vaginismus believe the condition to be the result of a castration fantasy. Whilst this may play a rôle in the development of some women, I noted that it did not emerge in the therapies of the women I interviewed, nor indeed my own.

A girl's susceptibility to vaginismus

Most child psychologists find that the phantasies I have described also occur in emotionally and physically normal girls. If such phantasies are common to us all, why then does vaginismus appear only in certain women? It may just be that some girls have a predisposition† towards a particular emotional condition.

If a girl's personality (ego) has strong natural defences it can help her overcome sexual fears. However, important hereditary factors† may have played a part in determining my emotional development and strength, predisposing me to a certain defence mechanism. It is known, for example, that some defence reflexes are transmitted between members of one family, explaining why some people have a special disposition to isolation or depression. I had an innate tendency to repression, forcing me to express emotional pain through my body – spasm.[12] Because of these hereditary factors I probably became fixed at a phase in development which the non-vaginismic woman has been able to pass through unknowingly.

A 'defense'* is a creative mechanism meant to protect me psychologically. It is an adaptation which has arisen out of fear and upset, operating in self-destructive as well as self-protective ways. Vaginal spasm attempts to keep out rejections and disappointments, but can also simultaneously prevent nourishment and love (including a penis) from coming in. The hidden part of my psyche has developed vaginismus to protect me from anticipated hurt, pain and

---

† We must be careful when using such terms as 'predisposition', 'hereditary factors' and 'susceptibility' because normally these imply some relation to biological symptoms or traits present since birth. However, with regard to vaginismus such meanings are irrelevant because what counts is the *attitudes* of a girl's parents, adults and contemporaries towards her sexuality. Therefore, when I refer to 'predisposition' and 'hereditary factors' it is to suggest that vaginismus evolves from both a combination of past and present circumstances. It is not something organic.

* I have chosen to spell defense with an 's' to differentiate between a *conscious* defence and an *unconscious* defense.

disappointment[13] and, in so doing, paradoxically prevents me from feeling loved.

Stress in sensitive phase of development

It is likely that I failed to overcome a normal stressful situation at a sensitive phase of development, possibly due to hereditary factors.[†] Stressful | situations (real or imagined) which occur during infantile and Oedipal phases of development can contribute to the onset of vaginismus. As a child I returned ('regressed') to an earlier stage where my personality had been less troubled. I thus took refuge in the stage of emotional growth where magical and fairytale thinking about my body and my vagina was typical.[14]

Ownership of one's vagina

> There seems to be an inability in the woman with vaginismus to acquire an ease of genital activity
> (Jill Curtis, Psychotherapist)

The path from girlhood to maturity is never an easy one, and the leap from being a little girl to entering the adult world is a major psychological hurdle.

When I was small I did not 'own' my body in the sense that I needed my mother to feed me, bathe me, dress me and even think for me. Depending on what sex we are, mother will choose whether our outfit is to be pink or blue. Perhaps we can recall the time when we suddenly knew we had to take care of our own bodies; this might have been when mother told us to wash our own necks; or perhaps it was the time when she no longer straightened our stockings or did our hair. In this sequence of unconscious events, the last piece of her body to be psychologically 'handed over' to a girl is her vagina. In a way, it symbolizes the final piece of her childhood.

Because of unconscious prohibitions transmitted from my parents, I may have felt unable to make this leap to owning my genitals with ease. If I felt I must remain an emotionally obedient daughter, I could not then seek my own lover as the ties to my parents caused me to doubt the

[†] See footnote page 61.

rightness of my needs and desires. I could not see myself as lover or wife, but merely as their little girl.

This ability to own one's vagina marks womanhood in psychosexual terms. If the path to emotional maturity is such that a girl feels guilty at no longer being the dutiful daughter, then she may be too anxious to leave childhood. In a psychological sense I remained that child whose vagina did not yet belong to me to enjoy, own or use without parental permission.

The adult as our model

In order to aspire to maturity and acquire my own sexuality, I needed to psychologically own my vagina. As well as negotiating this difficult path, I also needed (like all children) to admire and envy the adults around me enough to wish to be like them, emulate them, and finally join their world.

However, if the gap between my admiration and wish to be like them becomes too wide (because of overwhelming envy, persecutory phantasies or a hostile environment) then the necessary psychological growth is unable to take place. Biologically I reached adulthood, but was never able to psychologically acquire my vaginal maturity as my jealousy and envy of adults was too overwhelming.

When communications are unintentionally negative

Early perceptions of my parents may also have been crucial since their characters and personalities largely determined attitudes which existed in my home. In this way parents may consciously or unconsciously communicate their fears and anxieties:

> I suppose the belief that I took on board was that little girls don't have sex . . . so actually I'm being 'good' at the moment because I'm not having sex
> (Jan)

Because such messages tend to be more intensely transmitted to first-born or only-children, it's not uncommon to discover that, like me, many women with vaginismus are either the eldest in a family, an only daughter or an only child.

My mother's feelings about her body and sexuality strongly influenced how I came to feel. If a mother unconsciously stifles our natural curiosity about our bodies, this may instill in us that our vaginas are forbidden, mysterious and unwholesome territory. It should be understood that much of this negative conditioning, heavily influenced by mother's psychology and social factors, takes place in a gentle and well-intentioned way, rarely meant to harm or instill fear. I recall my mother telling me she disliked and couldn't insert tampons. Though this was never meant to frighten, it nevertheless resulted in negative feelings, compounding an already developing fear about inserting anything painlessly into my vagina.

> A fairly common thing that vaginismic women report is that they got stuck when they first tried to use tampons. The girl who gains confidence to do this and manages it has a tremendous boost to her confidence. For the girl who doesn't manage it, it's devastating because her fantasy is that she's either different to her friends or that she's too small
> (Dr Anne Mathieson, Medical Hypnotherapist)

Diverse differences of opinion are expressed by specialists as to the causes of vaginismus relating to the home. Some report that vaginismus is the result of a sexually repressed upbringing, but just as many refute this, stating that women who've had repressed childhoods are more likely to be generally sexually unresponsive and anorgasmic than to develop vaginismus. On the contrary, women who have vaginismus are often found to be very sexual, not inhibited as might be expected if their backgrounds were repressive.

The language of the vagina

The link between my development and my subsequent fantasies was a crucial one to make in understanding and treating my vaginismus, because the unconscious anxieties I had developed, for whatever reasons, were directly related to the onset of vaginismus. A specific fantasy a woman expresses can often be the key to understanding and treating spasm.[15] When I say something about my vagina, I may be saying something similar about my innermost fears and desires, giving clues to the origins of vaginismus. In Chapter Five we'll see how often women make the same claims about their feelings: they fear the vagina is too small, they claim to be ignorant about sex and their body, they fear intercourse will be painful, they fear they will be damaged. These are recurrent themes which we express over and over again.

But why, you may ask, are we expressing how we feel in this particular way? Could it be that if there is a part of ourselves inside of us that feels isolated, unloved, hidden, rejected, abandoned and infantile, yet remains unknown to us, this is the only way we can express such emotions:

'My vagina is too small'

Are we really saying that the adult in us is too small? Perhaps our wants, needs and unnurtured selves make us feel too small, too young, too undeveloped and too vulnerable.

'My vagina is a dark and dirty place'

Are we really saying that the sexy sides of our natures/our emotional needs and desires are dark, dirty, need cleaning up or merit apology?

'I wasn't told about sex. I knew my parents did it but I never felt I could'

Are we really saying that we need our parents' blessing, encouragement and permission to have desires and needs?

'Intercourse will be painful, I'll be damaged and torn'

Are we really saying that our desires for love and intimacy are also dangerous, damaging, overwhelming and need controlling?

'The thought of being penetrated makes me want to retch/feel sick'

Are we really saying that our needs and desires are too much for us to digest, that it's too soon to take them inside us because we aren't ready?

We can see how vaginal spasm is very much a metaphor for our innermost fears and feelings regarding our needs and desires. However, none of us will be using our bodies unconsciously to express the same thing, nor do we share the same language:

> There are common themes in women's psychology about being fearful of intimacy, feeling unentitled to love. But what the particulars are for each woman will be totally individual
> (Susie Orbach, Psychotherapist)

The developmental aspects show us that vaginismus isn't necessarily the result of wilful inadequate care or love from parents. It has far more to do with the complex combination of;

- our inherent predisposition
- our psychological development
- our personality
- the personalities of our caregivers
- their social conditioning
- our perceptions

Dr Thexton further highlights this last point:

> It's the girl's perceptions of her family and relationships rather than what they do. Sometimes it can be the most unexpected women who have vaginismus in that they appear to have had healthy, happy mothers, lovely opportunities and loving relationships .... and surprisingly find they have this problem
> (Dr Robina Thexton, Member Inst. Psychosexual Medicine)

PART II
TRAUMATIC

A trauma is a powerful incident or psychological shock which can sometimes have a lasting effect upon our well-being.

Though not cited as a major cause of vaginismus, trauma may have played a part in the onset of spasms in some women.

Aftermath of rape

> I was first raped at 16 . . . but I don't know whether I had vaginismus before that
> (Jan)

> I've treated women who had great problems after rape, so vaginismus can definitely develop after this
> (Dr Robina Thexton, Member Inst. Psychosexual Medicine)

As well as Dr Thexton, other doctors have confirmed to me that vaginismus can develop in a woman previously not suffering from spasm following a trauma such as rape. In addition, if rape is committed upon a very young girl before her sexual maturity has been allowed to develop, the effects can be so disturbing that the victim's psychosexual makeup may be damaged.

Aftermath of child sexual abuse

Vaginismus as a consequence of child sexual abuse is rarely mentioned in current medical literature. However, perhaps its absence is a reflection that as a general issue child abuse has been greatly suppressed in the past. Only in more recent years has such an issue become more openly discussed and widely accepted. Doctors and therapists confirm that whilst only a small number of sufferers have been sexually abused as children, it can nevertheless be a cause of vaginismus.

> We have to be careful and say that not all women who have vaginismus have been sexually abused. However, many of the women we work with have

developed spasm as a result of their being sexually abused as a child
(Richard Johnson, Director, Incest Crisis Line)

Brutal first-time sex

Brutal or painful early sexual experience, perhaps with a clumsy or insensitive lover, may also set the stage for vaginismus:

One woman had a rather brutal first husband, after which she couldn't make love the second time around and came for help
(Dr Robina Thexton, Member. Inst. Psychosexual Medicine)

Painful vaginal examinations

Sometimes the causes of vaginismus are said to be 'iatrogenic', meaning that the symptom has been aggravated or even induced in a woman as the result of a doctor's words or actions:

Of the three women I've seen today, two have been very badly hurt by a previous cervical smear and examination which has compounded the problem for them
(Dr Robina Thexton, Member Inst. Psychosexual Medicine)

Traumatic pelvic examinations are cited as being contributing factors, if not a sole cause, of vaginismus. This may occur when an unsympathetic or clumsy doctor performs an internal without sufficient care or sensitivity to a woman's feelings.

One doctor comments with dismay about such examinations:

I think doctors have quite a lot to answer for in the area of vaginismus. In the study that we (IPM) did, we asked women if they'd had a previous traumatic penetrative experience, not just vaginal but also rectal. A lot of dental treatment can also be transferred

down to this part of the body. The number of women
we met who'd had things said to them by doctors like
'You're a bit small . . . you'll have trouble when you
get married' . . . and then the fear grows and grows
(Dr Katharine Draper, Member Inst. Psychosexual
Medicine)

In the same way, a nurse-therapist registers her concern
and surprise at the insensitivity of some procedures:

I feel doctors in VD clinics must not always assume the
woman has been sexually active. One sufferer had not
had proper penetration, but was a contact with a man
who was found to have gonorrhoea. She went along to
a clinic where they carried out lengthy tests whilst she
was still a virgin. It was so traumatic that it took two
years for us to work through together(Barbara Lamb,
Nurse Psychosexual Counsellor)

One doctor I saw, hoping he would be able to help me but
unable to tell him my real problem, attempted to introduce
his finger into my vagina (as I'd complained of 'swelling
down there'). On seeing my difficulty he angrily prized my
legs apart and admonished me for being so childish. He
then added 'as a married woman you really ought to know
better'. Why was this doctor totally unable to recognise
spasm, even in a woman so obviously vaginismic as me?

Whilst such an experience didn't cause my vaginismus,
the trauma of being subjected to a brutal examination, both
verbally and physically, merely reinforced my fears about
either telling anyone or allowing anybody inside. So how
can we prevent iatrogenic vaginismus? One way is firstly
to point out to doctors and nurses (ideally during training)
that vaginismus may actually be created by a rough
physical examination or an insensitive approach. Another
is to suggest that when conducting vaginal examinations
the use of the word 'small' should be avoided in a woman's
presence.

Our birth experience

Not so long ago it was believed that the unborn child had
no feelings or thoughts in its mother's womb, and that it

only began to feel and think once it was a few weeks old. However, much more is now known about its emotional life and the effects birth can have on a baby's development. This might seem far-fetched, but if we consider that trauma in early childhood can affect us, why not something even earlier like, say, birth trauma?

In 1966 a French obstetrician, Frederick Leboyer, announced to a mostly sceptical medical world that he was convinced the emotional environment of birth had a profound impact and lifelong effects on a person. In 1974 his book *Birth Without Violence* laid the groundwork for a new awareness and sensitivity surrounding both mother and baby's birth experience. Leboyer demonstrated that the quieter, the more gentle a birth was, the more close and well-adjusted were the baby and its mother. He also claimed that his naturally-delivered babies fared better and were successful in later life.

> One of the causes of vaginismus can be birth traumas, which women sometimes go back to in hypnosis. You see, the first thing we ever learn about the vagina is going through mother's, and if that's a truly terrifying experience a woman may be left with the feeling that the vagina is a very dangerous place
> (Dr Anne Mathieson, Medical Hypnotherapist)

It doesn't automatically follow that a long, arduous and painful labour will produce spasm, because generally no one specific event will cause vaginismus. Re-Birthing Groups* have shown us that our ideas and feelings surrounding birth are very personal and will have different connections for different women. Some women when talking about their births don't even speak about the vagina, for example. One psychoanalyst said that he uses a

---

* Re-Birthing is a simple, subtle and powerful breathing experience putting a woman in touch with the pleasure of being alive, and allowing her to see her birth as an exciting, if frightening, interruption into the world. It is a cumulative process carried out over periods of weeks and months. A woman lies down and breathes, usually in the presence of a professionally trained Re-Birther. For two hours or more she breathes (called 'Conscious Connected Breathing') to help her release the panic of her first breath. In her breathing she reveals her basic attitudes toward

woman's imagery, fantasies or dreams about her birth as metaphors. For instance, if she imagines she was crushed and suffocated whilst in mother's birth canal, this would be interpreted by the analyst as the 'crushing, suffocating adult' who wouldn't let her have her own thoughts.

As yet there's no scientific evidence to prove or disprove that birth trauma can contribute to emotional problems. However, I feel that any fantasies or imagery we have surrounding our birth should be seen as an enriching collection of material which we and our therapist may work through. In this way, a woman's ideas about her entry into the world may be seen as yet another symbol and metaphor for her innermost fears and feelings.

Not all women who are exposed to trauma go on to develop vaginismus and the occurrence of spasm in a woman previously not suffering seems to imply she is somehow inherently predisposed to vaginismus. Perhaps the tendency to spasm remains dormant until triggered by the psychological effects of any event such as those outlined here.

PART III
RELATING TO PEOPLE IN OUR LIVES AND THE ENVIRONMENT ('RELATIONAL')

Causes of vaginismus are said to be 'relational' when the onset of spasm is connected to a person or situation outside our control. For example, vaginismus may occur if we feel hostile towards our lover, or if the society or environment we live in is intrusive and unsupporting. Here a doctor illustrates the effects on a woman whose status has suddenly changed:

> Vaginismus is surprisingly common for people who have been living together, not married, and they have a

life and gradually her breath restores itself to the balance and harmony it would have known had it not been for the trauma of that first gasp. She can then experience breathing as spontaneously cleansing rhythm rather than a fearful controlled machine. Positive effects have been to ease stressful situations by producing an intuitive sigh of release instead of breath-taking panic. Relationships may also become easier, safer and committed, partly because they're so often controlled by unconscious fear of separation, caused by the memory of leaving mother's womb.[16]

wedding ceremony and then it starts. That always needs
quite a lot of understanding
(Dr Robina Thexton, Member Inst. Psychosexual Medicine)

PARTNERS

Personally I feel that for some women the sexual partner
can consciously or unconsciously provide the fuel to
ignite her own deepest anxieties
(Lorna Guthrie, Jungian Analyst)

During my research I came across the opinion that our lovers
can either contribute to, cause or maintain our vaginismus.

If we think again about a little girl's development, a
woman's vaginismus may be seen as an expression of a
disturbed earlier relationship. In a way, spasm is an answer to
or defense against an unresolved conflict with a key figure (or
figures) in her life. However, her partner/lover/husband is
not necessarily the key figure. She may transfer her conflicts
(with mother or father) to *every* sexual partner, so that he (or
she, as in the case of a gay woman) then becomes an innocent
player in her scenario.[17] This does not imply that a partner is
never responsible or connected to a woman's vaginismus. I do
feel, though, that when looking at the partner we also have to
take into account a woman's earlier relationships which
shape her choice of and feelings towards a current lover.

*Can a partner cause vaginismus and can vaginismus cause
impotence?*

Masters and Johnson report that vaginismus has a common
association with primary impotence in the partner (a man
who has no previous experience of erection). They add that
where primary impotence and vaginismus exist in a
relationship it is often difficult to be sure whether spasm
existed prior to unsuccessful attempts at intercourse or
whether it developed secondarily because of frustration at
the man's impotence. In other words, can vaginismus
cause impotence or can impotence cause vaginismus?[18]

The man can become sensitized to the pain or
difficulty so that he's frightened of penetrating

eventually, but I think this happens out of the experience that he has . . . he doesn't actually bring that to the relationship
(Dr Paul Brown, Consulting Clinical Psychologist)

Masters and Johnson further report that if a man has severe premature ejaculation, then his partner can develop vaginismus through repeated frustrated attempts at lovemaking.[19]

However, I do not believe that the male partner is likely to be the main cause of vaginismus, but rather that he may trigger off causes lying dormant. In my experience, it was the *emotional* relationship between my husband and myself which suffered most from the effects of my vaginismus.

Perhaps because Masters and Johnson only treated couples with sexual difficulties, they neglected to notice the effects vaginismus has on a relationship holistically, only concentrating on the way spasm affects couples sexually.

Can a partner maintain vaginismus?

If a woman's lover has not caused her vaginismus, then it has been suggested that he can maintain it. One therapist states that in most cases he sees the role of the husband as an important contributing factor in the maintenance, if not the cause, of vaginismus. He observes that some husbands unconsciously collude in maintaining their wife's vaginismus if they themselves have unresolved fears and anxieties about sex.[20] On the other hand,

I haven't found this to be true. I've seen so many men help their partners with vaginismus that in no way are they colluding or maintaining her spasm
(Barbara Lamb, Nurse Psychosexual Counsellor)

The view that a lover maintains vaginismus assumes a man has power over his partner to a degree which doesn't seem plausible.

I think it's preferable to avoid making such generalisations about both the woman and her partner. Whilst some men may unconsciously maintain vaginismus (by perhaps not encouraging her to seek help), there are just as many men who will not.

Are partners all alike in terms of personality?

Again, a common view is that the man who chooses a woman with vaginismus is generally overly kind and gentle, passive and un-pushy, and usually has sexual problems of his own. This implies that in some way a man unconsciously 'knows' and chooses a woman who can't allow penetration because he has unresolved conflicts about his sexuality.

In contrast, the majority of doctors and therapists I met did not find this description of partners to be generally true. One therapist said that this is a particularly bad generalisation since he sees plenty of marriages where the man may be passive and gentle without his partner having vaginismus. He also remarked that he does not feel vaginismus has anything to do with the degree of gentleness or kindness that a husband demonstrates towards his wife:

> I remember one man where his wife's vaginismus caused tremendous stress but brought out the most loving side of him. However, I don't think it was because his wife had vaginismus; I think any distress that she had had would have caused the same loving response
> (Dr Paul Brown, Consulting Clinical Psychologist)

Another doctor told me that any sexual problems which from time to time cropped up in a relationship did so as a totally unexpected problem in what she would call a 'normal pairing'. In other words, she did not see any difference between the vaginismic women's partners and the other partners amongst her patients.

It's quite possible that a woman with vaginismus might unconsciously select a partner with kind and tolerant qualities on the somewhat mistaken hope and assumption that being so gentle he will hurt her less during intercourse. However, this is not evidence that only weak, impotent, timid, non-assertive men with hidden anxieties about their sexual role and potency are attracted to women who have vaginismus and therefore perpetuate their spasms. This view seems to rely upon the assumption that any lover of a vaginismic woman who fails to conform to the stereotypical 'macho', extrovert, strong, male image is somehow inherently attracted to that woman because she is unable to allow penetration. Disappointingly, it highlights the fact that sexist images of 'normal' male behaviour continue to be used as guidelines. Again, I prefer not to generalise. Whilst some partners will be overly kind and patient, just as many will not be.

Supporting my view, one study concludes that there is striking diversity in the nature of vaginismic women, their partners and the relationships between them.[21]

> The husbands cover a wide spectrum. They may be strong or weak, confident or unsure and some are angry and fed up whilst others are protective and supportive.
> (Dr Anne Mathieson, Medical Hypnotherapist)

However, it became apparent during my interviews that the majority of sex therapists view the role of the partner of the vaginismic woman with great importance. This probably explains why traditional sex therapy generally only accepts couples and not just the woman who has the vaginismus.

> Time and time again we've seen that couples, where the woman has vaginismus, have kind of chosen each other. Where there is vaginismus in a relationship, the difficulty appears to be all with the woman but in reality there often is some difficulty with her partner. This becomes apparent when he starts experiencing erectile difficulties, although the woman now is able to allow penetration
> (Alison Clegg, Sex Therapy Training Officer, National Marriage Guidance Council)

One sex therapist says he feels that a man has to be somehow 'different' if he continues in a relationship where the vaginismus is uncured and ongoing; another said that if a man waits years and years without having intercourse then the sufferer might need to ask herself why he is doing that.

The notion that there is a link between vaginismus and male impotence does not explain why women in gay relationships also suffer from vaginismus. Since vaginismus isn't confined to the heterosexual woman, it follows that the general assumptions made about her partner may be erroneous.

Emotional not sexual compatibility between couples

Our lovers are generally suspected of having problems of impotence, sexual identity or low sex-drive, but this assumption seems to arise out of a belief that the sexual problem of the woman is somehow mirrored in the man she is with. But is vaginismus truly about sexual receptivity? Isn't it more about emotional receptivity?

As one psychotherapist explains:

> The view that partners are impotent assumes that vaginismus doesn't happen in lesbian relationships and assumes it is only about penises. Whereas in fact to me it's so little about the penis and so much more about the woman and her capacity to feel loved
> (Susie Orbach, Psychotherapist)

Susie Orbach then went on to challenge the view that partners of sufferers are a certain type of personality, and the general assumption that they 'fit' psychologically together. She says that although men are scared of their own sexuality and may feel alarmed by vaginismus, she nevertheless believes the 'fit' between couples is much more of an emotional one:

> One might, for instance, have a man who really wants to give love but doesn't know how to do it
> (Susie Orbach, Psychotherapist)

As if to confirm this, Frances describes the unconscious mutual attraction between her and a partner:

> I suspect that I tend to attract men at my own level of psychosexual development, who want to be given to,

not to give
(Frances)

We may all make unconscious choices about our partners, and there's no real way of knowing how that choice is affected by the fact that we have vaginismus. I do feel that the choices we make regarding a sexual partner relate more to an emotional compatibility, not a sexual one. Again, Frances explains how she believes relating intimately begins at the breast. She then describes how the problems of basic nurturing at the start of her life have unconsciously affected her emotional choice of men:

> What causes me much despair is that I think I seek a mother in a man. Unless he gives me all the love I've missed, I don't want to give anything
> (Frances)

Friedman found that although a high proportion of husbands in his study were described by wives as 'kind, considerate and passive', these traits had no prognostic significance.[22] The same study also found that the husband's sexual potency showed no relationship to the outcome of therapy.[23]

It appears that neither the lover's personality, gender or sexual abilities play an important role, and I would only consider the personality of a partner to be of significance if it was found that this had a detrimental effect on either the woman's well-being or the outcome of therapy.

The interplay between us and our lovers should be viewed simultaneously with other influences on our lives, but the roles they play should not be considered to assume significant proportions in either the causes or the outcome of treatment for vaginismus.

WOMEN IN SOCIETY

'Relational' causes does not just mean the relationship between a woman and someone in her life: the society or environment in which she lives may also have a part to play in the onset of vaginismus. Vaginismus may, therefore, be related to wider social issues.

Situating vaginismus in society

Whilst it isn't within the scope of this book to fully discuss the role of women in society, nor how we are portrayed, in a way these issues can't be separated or ignored when looking at vaginismus:

> I don't think it's possible to divorce society or culture from the body image a woman has of herself. If a woman in this society has no power over her body or her life, then all she can do is say 'No' with her body (Anne Dickson, Sexuality/assertiveness trainer and author)

Much of women's experiences, history and hurt have gone unheard in the world. Indeed, this is exactly how it felt when nobody was able to see or hear my pain around vaginismus before I received help. In the same way, women's place in society and its effects may go unnoticed in some therapeutic approaches to vaginismus.

Freud's patriarchal view of feminine psychology

During research I became resentful and upset by pre-feminist analytic writings which don't acknowledge a girl's difficulty in entering the social world, unlike her brother's encouragement and ability to achieve autonomy. Mother's social conditioning and how it influences her daughter's psychological make-up is also rarely mentioned. Since this relationship is central to our development it would seem crucial not to ignore that mother's conditioning was influenced by her parents, who themselves were products of a society which also constrained women.

> Although social factors are entirely entwined in a woman's development, it is the particulars of an individual that are going to be affected. However, that child is growing up in a culture within a family, and that culture, that family and that mother's feelings and behaviours are determined by the structure of our society
> (Susie Orbach, Psychotherapist)

The feminist approach does not simply reject Freudian* concepts. Rather, it embodies most traditional theories but also views woman's position in society and its effects on her emotional makeup. Feminist therapy believes social factors shouldn't be ignored mainly because viewing a girl's psychosexual development through the eyes of patriarchy may risk missing the total picture of her development and predisposition to vaginismus. This might, for example, take the form of indiscriminately viewing father, as Freud did, to be the central figure in every girl's psychological development. As we will see in Jenny's treatment, feminist therapy whilst taking the lead from the client, finds itself ultimately concentrating on the complex issues surrounding the mother-daughter relationship. A feminist approach tends to refrain from describing a sufferer as 'immature' or 'childish'. This approach also does not believe, as Freud did, that instinctual drives of sex and aggression shape our psychology. It is felt that the drive is far more for intimacy, love, contact and relationships with other human beings. Feminist understanding of a woman's psychology centres around the knowledge that we are expected to be emotionally dependent upon others, yet paradoxically find ourselves deferring to and nurturing everybody else. One of the inevitable results of this is the ensuing ambivalent and unsatisfying feelings that may be transmitted from mother to daughter. Consequently, inside both mother and infant remains the little girl whose needs for nurturing and acceptance are never being fully met.

Vaginismus as the body's protest

My need to understand and explain vaginismus led me to become interested in the origins of women's other problems. There is one in particular which seems similar to vaginismus, and that is anorexia nervosa. We might even

*Freud's theories and concepts remain the cornerstone of all psychotherapies and his contribution to the understanding of men and women's psychology has been invaluable. However, in his defence, Freud was very much a product of this time and it is precisely this Victorian background which is believed to have influenced and coloured his view of women.

call vaginismus 'genital anorexia'. In her book *Hunger Strike*, Susie Orbach also makes a link between these two. She writes that although the particular makeup of a woman's psychology predisposes her to develop the anorectic symptom she might not necessarily have taken up this condition had she lived in a different historical period. Her psychology may have more in common with the pre-orgasmic or 'frigid' woman found two or three decades ago. Such women were unable to experience sexual pleasure expressing this in a withdrawn attitude, involuntary closedness and, in the extreme, the inability to open up and let go both psychologically and physically (spasm). The symptom of vaginismus may be the solution that our psychological makeup has sought as a means of defence.[24]

Hunger Strike further explains why women use their bodies to express a protest. To quote the author:

> We see that living within prescribed boundaries is the reason why our bodies become the vehicle for a whole range of expressions that have no other medium . . . we are forced to speak with our bodies.[25] Whenever woman's spirit has been threatened, we have taken control of our bodies as an avenue of self-expression. If her body is the site of her protest, then equally her body is the ground on which the attempt for control is fought.[26]

The sexual freedom of contemporary woman is allegedly not so constrained as in Freud's time or in the 1950s, but similar social and psychological factors may be causing 'spasm' to occur around eating. Perhaps this is because the objectification of women's body and her image is today linked far more strongly with food, fashion and weight-gain than ever it was in Freud's era.

> Women don't have social equality. Men have a place in the world where they've been brought up to be expansive and go out and do things. Women have been consistently told to constrain themselves. To constrain the vagina is consequence of that constraint (Susie Orbach, Psychotherapist)

Women are still second-class citizens and it has made
women contract
(Sarah)

Feminist approaches to eating disorders have successfully
led the way in working therapeutically with such
problems. This same approach can help the vaginismic
woman look at why she is unable to allow penetration,
what it means to her, and the social pressures placed upon
her.

In a feminist context the symptoms of anorexia nervosa
and vaginismus are seen to be the body's way of protesting
that a woman's needs for love, comfort, security and
acceptance have never been fully met. However, it may be
far more complex than this. Referring to *Good Mother . . .
Bad Mother* (page 57), it may not simply be that baby's
needs have gone unmet so much as that a disturbance in
the developing psychological processes has caused baby to
feel that love and care are unavailable to her. Her anger and
upset in not being able to feel the love may thus obliterate
the loving responses that may genuinely be there.

Creating a defensive boundary

It's not only feminists who believe that vaginismus may be
connected with women's social and political status. Freud,
too, was aware that social influences play a part in the
construction of the feminine personality.[27] If we look at
vaginismus within this wider context in the way Susie
Orbach does with anorexia nervosa, it could be suggested
that vaginal spasm is illustrating the effects of patriarchal
society on us, namely our fear of being invaded by men
and of losing our identity. To prevent this invasion we
create a defensive boundary using our bodies (the one
boundary we feel certain about). Unconsciously we see
intercourse as the penetration of our boundaries, and the
protection from invasion manifests physically in
vaginismus.[28]

Body insecurity

But how do social constraints on a woman set vaginismus

in motion? The impact of patriarchy on the mother-daughter relationship is profound and may be the key to why vaginismus is prone to develop. If mother is the unconscious transmitter of an 'inferior' psychology of women, then this is where, as little girls, we first learned what our social role would be. This process occurred at the same time as we were developing a psychological sense of our selves. Because of my mother's position in the world it was hard for her to give me feelings that my body was an OK and safe place to live, develop and be expansive, as well as to eat whatever I wanted:

> Our mothers were rarely brought up to like sex. Thus they didn't have any way to transmit that sex is all right to the next generation. Our generation has the message that sex is OK, but it doesn't feel OK
> (Susie Orbach, Psychotherapist)

Because a mother can't do any of this she may already be very hesitant about her daughter's exploration of her vagina. If mother has grown up with the negativity of the 'curse', images of slimness, and a submission to sex and dominance, then she is going to need to unconsciously convey to us that we, too, must watch out in these areas. Could it be that the same social forces are at work between mothers and daughters which make particular women susceptible to vaginismus, just as others are to anorexia nervosa?

Women and the Media

Advertisements, magazines, TV and films bombard men and women with images of how women should feel, look and act, many in a sexual way:

> Socially we are supposed to have penetrative sex at an increasingly younger age
> (Dr Patricia Gillan, Consultant Psychologist)

We are visually stereotyped as 'perfect' and 'available'. Could the woman with vaginismus be unconsciously expressing her protest about such images, her desire not to compete with them, and her consequent refusal to allow any (as she sees it) dominating force inside her? So, too, if society's unconscious messages to women are always 'don't do this' and 'mustn't do that', then could vaginismus be the only protest we can make about *not* allowing something inside us unless it's on our own terms?

Female sexuality and intercourse

A Dutch 'emancipatory therapist' (one who works totally free from social constraints imposed on women by convention) reports on research into women's attitudes towards penetration.[29] One study reveals that approximately two-thirds of happily married women wish to change their love patterns, i.e. to have less intercourse, make love in ways not immediately directed to penetration, and have more warmth and involvement with their partners. Some women said they never initiated sex for fear of intercourse, and we are speaking here about non-vaginismic women! Further research reveals hierarchies of preferences during lovemaking. Highest on the list was emotional experiences, feeling accepted and loved by the partner and an ability to love and really be oneself. Much less important was penetration.* These findings imply there is little difference between the way vaginismic and non-vaginismic women feel about penetration, in that *we all need to feel known, loved and accepted* before allowing anyone inside us. † In this way the gap closes between a woman who has vaginismus and one who does not.

Men's sexual likes are often stereotyped and so appear to differ from women's, with warmth, involvement and the expression of love-words generally having far more importance for us than for men. However, it may be that:

– The intimate relationship between infant daughter and caregiver is difficult to negotiate and quite different from that between mother and son, leading us to feel

---

* My feeling is that this reported disinterest in penetration should not be interpreted literally as a dislike of intercourse. Perhaps what the research reflects more is a woman'a inability to feel loved, and naturally this might make her unhappy about letting a penis inside her.
† When my body said 'no' to my partner this did not necessarily mean he was the person I felt didn't know, love or accept me. Such unconscious feelings stemmed from much earlier relationships, i.e. with mother/father.

unknown, unloved, unlovable and unaccepted

- Because of this, our psychology develops differently to men's, which may be the reason why it seems less important for a man to need to love and feel loved before engaging in intercourse.

Do social factors influence vaginismus?

The ideas developed by some feminist therapists clearly suggest that social forces may contribute to the occurrence of vaginal spasm. Our status in an oppressed world may certainly compound our vulnerability to vaginismus and also potentially damage the mother-daughter relationship.

Mother's social conditioning combined with her psychology may make it painfully difficult or even impossible for her to allow her daughter:

- the rightfulness of her needs
- entitlement to love and security
- ownership of her vagina

PART IV
PHYSICAL CAUSES

Excluding any deformities of the vagina such as an abnormally small vaginal opening ('introitus') or even its absence, there may be a physical reason for the onset of vaginismus.

For example, spasm may develop after a long period of undiagnosed and consequently untreated painful inter-course. (The causes and treatment of dyspareunia have been described in Chapter Three).

Note: For a deeper understanding of an infant girl's developing sense of self and boundaries, I suggest reading *Understanding Women* by Susie Orbach & Luise Eichenbaum and also the chapter *Breeding of Body Insecurity* in *Hunger Strike*.

Untreated dyspareunia is going to end up in vaginismus quite often. It might have been an infection of thrush which would make intercourse painful, and from then on there's spasm. Vaginismus is also very common after the birth of a baby
(Dr Robina Thexton, Member Inst. Psychosexual Medicine)

But how does an infection cause vaginismus? It is simply that anticipation of pain every time during penetration thus leads to spasm. If, however, the pain continues even after the local infection has been treated and there is still no physical explanation for it, then it's possible the vaginismus is being sustained by psychological conflicts and requires to be treated psychotherapeutically.

Vaginismus is therefore generally developmental, the causes of which are predominantly psychological, rarely physical, in origin.

CHAPTER FOUR

Seeking Help

CAN VAGINISMUS BE RESOLVED WITHOUT PROFESSIONAL HELP?

There are varying degrees of vaginismus ranging from mild to severe, so the degrees of help necessary to resolve it will be reflected in the severity of the muscle spasm.

> Depending upon the causes, some women can resolve vaginismus themselves. They might, for instance, resolve it with a very understanding partner
> (Barbara Lamb, Nurse Psychosexual Counsellor)

Carol was able to resolve vaginismus herself. She explains how her mother terrified her about falling pregnant before she was married and Carol believes she developed vaginismus as a consequence. After a series of unconsummated relationships she suddenly stopped worrying about falling pregnant and, as a result, found herself able to allow complete intercourse with her next lover. She concludes:

> In my case all I did in the end was to stop worrying . . . it was a shame it took me so long
> (Carol)

One leading women's magazine has produced a leaflet on vaginismus, beautifully written by a sensitive gynaecologist.[1] The leaflet guides a woman step-by-step through a self discovery exercise to help her gain confidence in stages that her vagina isn't too small or abnormal, and to help her familiarize herself with this part of her body which often remains mysterious for many of us. Compared to the penis, the vagina is partly a concealed and internal organ, so many women who don't have vaginismus may harbour irrational fantasies about its nature. This doesn't mean they are seriously disturbed if they have such feelings: it's only when the fear becomes so exaggerated that it prevents penetration that such fantasies need to be explored. It's important though to be aware that for some of us, self examination may not provide the total answer in resolving vaginismus. Jean describes her difficulties even after she was able to explore her vagina:

> The specialist taught me how to explore inside myself . . . I could do it when she was there, but not at home. I still remained terrified of a penis and a tampon, despite this, so the treatment fizzled out again . . . I felt it was my fault
> (Jean)

On their own, exploration and educational techniques may be rather superficial and might not resolve vaginismus if a woman's fantasies haven't been sufficiently understood and worked through. This demonstrates the gap between approaches which focus heavily on relaxing the vagina and those which do not. There may be little value in obeying a command to examine ourselves when the emotional wounds and defences behind the vaginismus haven't been sufficiently healed. Once the therapeutic (repair) process has given a woman an understanding, acceptance and comfort with her own self, she may find that of her own accord and wishes the desire to explore her vagina comes naturally. It requires a degree of self-love and trust to do this.

The knowledge that fantasies and fears of intimacy, love and dependency come in the way of our ability to allow penetration, and *not* our smallness or tightness is a far more meaningful acquisition in the long-run than simply being able to relax our vagina because we've been given a specific instruction to do so.

IF YOU SUSPECT VAGINISMUS WHEN SHOULD YOU SEEK HELP?

> My advice is to seek help as soon as possible . . . my vaginismus hung over me like a black cloud
> (Sarah)

Unfortunately, vaginismus may persist indefinitely if left untreated. My advice, therefore, is to seek help at the earliest opportunity because if it remains untreated then the subsequent stress inherent in any problem may only increase in time.

All the doctors and therapists stress the importance of seeking help early. One said that without intervention vaginismus often gets worse. Mostly they are concerned that the sufferer should feel she isn't alone in her struggle. However, as explained earlier, it's not always an easy step to take. It's painful to share vaginismus with someone else, but it can feel devastating sharing it with someone who doesn't have an understanding of the deep distress that such a condition creates. One psychotherapist told me how difficult it can be for a woman to come forward after so many years of pain. Clearly, she has an understanding of the fears around seeking help:

> A lot of women will have become embedded into the condition and might feel there's no hope anyway. If they do reach out, we are asking a lot of them. She is going to be afraid of being hurt, of being penetrated, and it's asking a lot of women to trust, and that's what psychotherapy is about
> (Jill Curtis, Psychotherapist)

Once we've made the decision to seek help then this can be seen as the first step in the process towards resolution. However, this alone will not be enough to produce the desired change. There has to be a willingness on our part to be active participants in the healing process. In attempts to relieve myself of the responsibility to overcome vaginismus, I would fantasise being seduced and penetrated by a complete stranger, indicating an illusory belief that 'someone else out there' could 'do it' to me and 'solve it for me'. In this way I became the passive recipient of a 'cure' rather than actively contributing to the solution. It was noticing how I closed up, went into spasm and couldn't take charge that I became more committed to my therapy and began to take responsibility for its outcome and success.

OBSTACLES CAN CREATE OPPORTUNITIES

We've all read stories in the press about professional misconduct between a patient and doctor. Happily, extreme cases such as these are generally rare. What is sadly more common is the cold, rushed and indifferent attitude of many general practitioners and doctors. This may be the result of an over-worked practice or a grossly under-funded health service, but the fact remains that I, and many other sufferers, will have experienced insufficient care and attention along the way. During the course of this book I met and corresponded with many sufferers. Painfully I listened to them recount their stories of misery, hopelessness, persever-ence and courage. Often the themes resonated with my own.

This isn't to imply that skilled, sensitive and effective help is unavailable to every woman with vaginismus. The practitioners who share their expertise so freely in this book are those who don't represent the practices, attitudes and responses of uncaring professionals. Nevertheless, I include the painful experiences of some women because assuming that there will be no problems when seeking help may lull us into thinking that sensitive help is always just around the corner. In reality it may be an uphill struggle.

> I went to so many doctors I can't remember all of them. We kept saying 'Help! We can't make love' . . . but there was no treatment offered
> (Jan)

> After a disastrous and tearful honeymoon I went to my GP. He was old, deaf and out of touch, and everyone in the waiting room could hear while I sobbed out my story. He gave me tranquillizers, but they didn't work
> (Jean)

Sadly, the path towards finding correct help for my condition led to many dead-ends with hopes being dashed and my suspicions that vaginismus was too great for anyone being confirmed. I hope that my experience will enable you to make a speedy, assertive and well-informed choice, unlike me.

Because I didn't know I had vaginismus, I didn't know how or with whom I should seek help, so I contacted a private Well Woman clinic in 1977. My first appointment was with a gynaecologist, as at the time they didn't employ anyone trained in psychosexual medicine. I was nervous and terrified. Although the doctor seemed to know what vaginismus was, he didn't know how to explore with me the underlying causes, nor how to treat it. Instead, his advice was simply to go away, relax and not worry too much 'because I don't know if you know this, but even animals find intercourse painful'. Not surprisingly, I left feeling hopeless and totally confused. As I made my way to the tube station I felt overwhelmed with despair and pain. I'd gone to a doctor (a woman's doctor) for help with vaginismus. Instead, I had not been seen, heard or understood at all, but rather given a bizarre suggestion about the way in which animals have sex. As the Northern line train approached the platform I very nearly threw myself underneath it.

> The first doctor I saw sent me away with a huge medical textbook on vaginismus with no offer of treatment. Because I was on anti-depressants the book was quite beyond my comprehension. All I can remember thinking is 'God, somebody else must have this' . . . knowing that I wasn't alone
> (Jan)

The following month I returned and saw a different gynaecologist. Although kind and sympathetic, and wanting to comfort me as I was crying, he didn't seem to grasp what vaginismus was at all, and reassuringly said 'Oh, it's very common to fear sex for the first time, in fact my own wife did. Just relax and leave it all up to your husband and it'll be fine'. He then promptly wrote me six months prescription for the Pill. On my way home I wept and thought how ironic it was that I was probably the only woman swallowing contraceptive pills who couldn't have sex.

Several years lapsed and I returned to the clinic again, this time seeing a more enlightened gynaecologist. Her planned 'behavioural' treatment was to insert glass penis-shaped objects ('dilators') of graduating size into my vagina until I could tolerate one the size of an erect penis. However, the severity of my vaginismus meant I was phobic about anything entering me, and was unable to tolerate a pelvic examination even allowing the tip of her finger.

Eventually, the doctor decided she could only examine me whilst anaesthetised. The entire procedure of being intravenously sedated and then later not being able to remember the insertion of a speculum* felt so brutal and inhumane that I wasn't able to return to the clinic, or to seek help with anyone else, until more than two years later.

Unrelenting the vaginismus continued, and in a final desperate attempt I contacted the clinic again in late 1981. This time I was very lucky. A family planning and psychosexually trained doctor (who was also an analytical psychotherapist) was doing part-time psychosexual sessions at the clinic. During our first meeting we discussed how his approach would be to explore my feelings and fears, not my vagina. This became a turning point in dealing with my vaginismus. Not just because at last I had discovered a method which felt more right than anything previously, but also because this doctor's attitude was so totally different. When I wept he didn't just reassure me to stop me from crying. Instead he acknowledged the pain and distress I was feeling and expressed his commitment in being able to help. For the first time I felt emotionally 'held' and understood.

The ability to hear a woman's pain

This doctor was hearing my pain. What I mean by this is not having a person say to me 'there there, it'll be all right' or even 'it's not that awful, after all, penetration isn't everything'. This would have been tantamount to telling me my problem wasn't that serious. Rather, my pain was given space and validation in that the doctor didn't rush in with the usual comforting aphorisms. He was simply hearing how terrible vaginismus made me feel in a way that no other doctor had been able to before.

We made an appointment to meet the following week and I sensed for the first time in my life that a positive step towards solving vaginismus had been taken that day. The relief in finding the right therapist is also illustrated by Jan:

> When I finally saw the clinical psychologist it was incredible. We worked through the past. . . . I actually

---

* A speculum is a metal instrument used to dilate the walls of the vagina to permit visual examination.

became the child
(Jan)

Sadly, others haven't been as fortunate. Many women simply give up searching for help after their vaginismus is repeatedly responded to inappropriately.

- I went to family planning next. They tried to examine me but were nonplussed at my terror and just said it'd all sort itself out

- I sobbed out my story to a marriage counsellor. She was young and suburban, and hadn't a clue

- I paid privately out of my small wage to see a psychiatrist. It was no help. He went in for long silences which I found threatening

- The doctor at the gynae. clinic I was sent to was harrassed. He felt I was being wilfully awkward and shouted at me when he couldn't examine me

- The nurses were silently accusing . . . thinking me very odd

- One doctor, when she found she couldn't give me an internal, slapped my legs and told me to come back when I'd grown up

- The last specialist I saw, three years ago, just thoroughly humiliated me. I felt so belittled I vowed never to go anywhere again

Echoing these experiences, one psychosexual doctor reports similar experiences of patients. She told me that due to a vaginal discharge, one woman first consulted her GP, but when the vaginismus prevented him from examining her he became so angry he sent her away. She then met with a very impatient family planning doctor who was also unable to examine her. Finally, as a last resort, she consulted a Harley Street specialist who gave her a general anaesthetic and took a smear. The anaesthetic only reinforced the idea that no-one could go near the woman's vagina without her being totally knocked out.

Though she is now receiving appropriate therapy, the doctor says that this last procedure has set the patient back even further.

There are unconscious processes at work in both sufferer and doctor which can contribute to our misery. For example, why in many cases is the woman not given information on results of the procedures? If drugs are used to reach our unconscious and the findings remain unexplained and undiscussed, we may assume there must be something deeply disturbing about what the doctor has discovered, compounding our despair even further. Jean tells of the time she was intravenously sedated and the fear she felt afterward about what her disclosures had unashamedly revealed:

> The psychiatrist took me into his clinic and gave me Pethadon* (sic) . . . wonderful! . . . I could have done anything! I talked totally uninhibitedly . . . heaven knows what I said or what they made of it. I was afraid to ask, and they didn't tell me, probably assuming I was afraid to know
> (Jean)

Another sufferer describes how she felt hopeless partly because a gynaecologist had given her that impression:

> He performed an internal under anaesthesia and confirmed vaginismus . . . but again he didn't refer me for help. That was the end of the discussion, so this compounded the feeling in me that I had vaginismus for life
> (Jan)

Looking back, it would have been far better if all of us had known in the first place how to make contact with the people we eventually worked with. It might have saved us years of wasted time, unnecessary pain and anguish. However, perhaps the difficult road I took helped me in the end to see what treatments were wrong for me and which were right. Maybe even the act of seeking help can be seen as part of the

---

* Jean is referring to Pethidine, an analgesic (pain killer) administered by injection into a muscle that can make us feel 'high'.

process rather than a means to an end in itself.

It is important to make an informed choice

> I wish I'd been given a choice . . . I would've chosen to
> see a sex therapist. I saw a programme on TV and liked
> the understanding and talking through rather (as in
> my case) just being stretched under anaesthetic and
> given dilators to take home and use
> (Sarah)

As the causes are multiple and the degrees of vaginismus
vary, there can be no one single way to help a sufferer. Each
of us responds to a different, special combination of
therapeutic treatments. At best, several techniques for
treating vaginismus may be used and an imaginative
doctor or therapist, as I hope many of us will be fortunate to
work with, will often amalgamate what s/he thinks will
work most successfully with you as an individual. Because
there is no one definitive course of treatment, the methods
used vary from hospital to hospital, clinic to clinic, doctor
to doctor. Not only do they vary in technique, but also in
quality. In view of the difficult and lengthy course I had to
steer in order to find appropriate help, I can't over-
emphasise the importance of knowing what treatments are
available and where they are. I hope this helps promote a
greater element of choice in your selection.

The most appropriate forms of treatment for vaginismus
tend to involve psychotherapeutic technique (known as
the 'talking treatment'). This method employs verbal
communication rather than the use of other means, such as
drugs or surgery. It is the process of talking that attempts to
unlock that part of us (the hidden part of our psyche) which
unconsciously controls the muscles in our vagina.
Although psychotherapy was originally developed to treat
individuals, it has now also been successfully adapted to
treat couples.

> Psychotherapy **can** have a part to play in the
> resolution of vaginismus, but I think it can't be seen as
> a 'cure all'. I'm always very worried about psychother-
> apy being seen like that. I am certain, though, it could

help many women reach their potential that can then
lead to a resolution
(Jill Curtis, Psychotherapist)

The importance of a professional organisation

My worry is for people who go to unqualified
therapists because at the moment there is nothing to
stop anyone from advertising in magazines
(Jill Curtis, Psychotherapist)

In the same way as you'd expect a doctor or a lawyer to be
qualified, always go to a qualified therapist. Unfortunately, anyone can advertise themselves as a psychotherapist, sex therapist or hypnotherapist in magazines and
newspapers without specified training, being subject to a
code of practice or being named in a central register of
practitioners. One psychotherapist shared her concern
with me about this situation and said that a conference has
been meeting annually over the course of several years to
try to achieve agreement about the description of the
profession 'psychotherapy'; members have recently
agreed to organise themselves according to their major
specialities. The ultimate aim of the conference is to
compile a code of ethics and a list of therapists. As this is
still some years away from completion, the advice given
here is to help protect your interests until such guidelines
become legal.

The safest routes to obtaining help are generally through
personal recommendation, via your general practitioner,
or through a recognised organisation (page 194). The fact
that a therapist is a member of an organisation is some
guarantee of competence and can also minimize the risk of
exploitation. A therapist can take advantage of a woman's
sexual and emotional vulnerability if he has not been
sufficiently trained or if his motives are not wholly
honourable. In the psychotherapeutic setting a woman
may share her intimate fears and fantasies; sometimes
erotic feelings will be aroused. It is important that a
therapist has integrity and is a member of an organisation
where he will be subject to some degree of regulation by

his colleagues.

How do we avoid the person who may lack the experience and qualifications? Whilst there's no foolproof method, there are some measures we can take as explained by Dr Brown:

> Any woman approaching a person who has got some expertise in a basic professional skill (such as doctor, social worker or psychologist) and who has also got some special interest in sexual difficulties can regard that such a person will be competent. Anyone who is advertising their services about curing clinical problems should be avoided like the plague
> (Dr Paul Brown, Consulting Clinical Psychologist)

To ensure the right course of therapy is undertaken, an initial assessment should generally be sought before a commitment is made to any particular method. This consultation (known as a 'clinical service') offers you the opportunity to meet with a therapist who may not be personally treating you but who will have the opportunity to talk over with you whether in his opinion therapy is going to help. The aim is to try and work out what is best for the patient. Contacting an institute, society or association of recognised practitioners ensures that an initial assessment will be offered as a matter of policy, whereas this might not be the case if you answered a therapist's advertisement.

As we should take care not to pigeon-hole the sufferer, so equally we should not have preconceived ideas about the best person with whom to seek treatment. It doesn't necessarily follow that because the origins of vaginismus might lie in our early development we need to seek the help of, say, a psychoanalyst:

> The most important thing always in anything to do with one's emotions is to go to someone you feel will listen in a knowledgeable, caring way so that a woman cay say what she wants to in her own time
> (Lorna Guthrie , Jungian Analyst)

As well as ensuring a person is sufficiently qualified, it's equally important to trust your feelings and use your intuition when choosing a therapist. I knew from the first consultation that my analyst felt right for me.

> It's very important that in seeking help a woman finds the person she trusts. She should choose her therapist as much as the therapist says he can help her
> (Dr Paul Brown, Consulting Clinical Psychologist)

The earlier help is sought, the better. Likewise, the more informed our choice, the easier it will be to actively participate in the healing process.

Who are the people who treat vaginismus?

Nowhere is the relationship between a woman and her doctor more important than in the treatment of vaginal spasm. It requires a degree of trust and openness to allow someone into our innermost thoughts and feelings. For many of us, the barriers, blocks and protective mechanisms (spasm) will consciously and unconsciously attempt to keep people out. These defenses not only protect us, but also keep out the people we love, want and need from the hidden part of our selves which we feel is destructive, devouring and bad. Possibly our doctor/therapist will come up against the same kind of defense mechanisms. Though professional qualifications are important, in the end a person's sensitivity, experience and awareness will generally shape the quality of the relationship between sufferer and helper. Much evidence exists to support the view that it's not the type of therapy that is crucial to the success or failure of a treatment . . . it is the therapist that counts.

There are a range of professionals treating vaginismus who come from varied disciplines. Since vaginismus may be a symptom of other deeper conflicts, it is important that the people we work with can assess the treatment possibilities. If, for example, vaginismus is not helped by self-exploration or reassurance, then the skills of a therapist are essential because examination of the less conscious factors behind the spasm is a highly technical and professional business.[2] Anyone who treats vaginismus, therefore, needs to have psychotherapy skills plus extensive knowledge of human emotions and behaviour. In fact, sexual therapy should always be taught in addition to, not in place of, other basic psychotherapeutic skills because mind and body are interrelated. A therapist should ideally always put the woman's needs first and adjust his method to suit each individual. It's quite possible, for example, that a psychoanalyst might refer a patient to a behavioural therapist and vice versa if he thought it would be a more appropriate way of treating her particular vaginismus.

The various professionals who may treat vaginismus with their backgrounds and particular areas of expertise are listed below. They will not necessarily have special expertise in treating vaginismus, so it's best to check first whether this is an area in which they are happy to work. I also list the additional qualifications they should have if they are to treat vaginismus.

ANALYTICAL PSYCHOLOGIST OR ANALYTICAL PSYCHOTHERAPIST

Medically or non-medically qualified person with experience in psychology, social work or related fields with training in analytical psychotherapy. Has undergone own psychoanalysis.

BEHAVIOURAL THERAPIST

Psychologist with training in psychosexual problems.

GENERAL PRACTITIONER/GYNAECOLOGIST

Doctor who also has special interest/training in psychosexual problems.

HOMOEOPATH

Graduate of homoeopathy who may be medical, non-medical or nursing, and accredited to a professional society.

HYPNOTHERAPIST

Doctor, psychologist or psychotherapist trained by one of the following:

- Society of Medical & Dental Hypnosis
- British Society of Experimental & Clinical Hypnosis
- Institute of Analytical Hypnotherapists
- The Society for Primary Cause Analysis by Hypnosis

PSYCHIATRIST

Doctor who also has special interest/training in psychosexual problems.

PSYCHOANALYST

Psychiatrist with psychoanalytic training. Has undergone own psychoanalysis.

PSYCHOTHERAPIST

Doctor who also has training in psychotherapy. Psychiatric social worker with training in psychotherapy. Psychologist (known as 'Dr') with training in psychotherapy. Graduate in related fields with training in psychotherapy.

SEX THERAPIST

Psychologist with training in sexual therapy. Marriage Guidance Counsellor with training in sexual therapy. Psychotherapist with training in sexual therapy. Family planning doctor with training in sexual therapy. Family planning nurse with training in sexual therapy. Psychiatric social worker with training in sexual therapy.

Note: For further reading and guidance on how to choose a psychotherapist or holistic practitioner see the excellent books *Talking To A Stranger* by Lindsay Knight and *How To Survive Medical Treatment* by Stephen Fulder. (Details on page 241).

CHAPTER FIVE

The Treatments and How They Work

WHAT ARE THE TREATMENTS FOR VAGINISMUS?

In contrast with the United States, in Britain there is still a stigma attached to any psychological problem which requires therapy, and vaginismus is no exception. The misconception that you must be middle class, rich, well-educated or neurotic to benefit from therapy may regrettably deter many from seeking the necessary help. As consumers of health services we may also find it a daunting task to select the most appropriate therapy. By describing each method as simply as possible I hope to demystify the process, dispel any unfounded myths and fears and enable you to make a choice.

Not one 'Royal Road' to the resolution

Many of the treatments I outline may seem to blur into one another. 'Sex therapy' is a generic term to describe any method that seeks to help a woman with a sexual problem, and a combination of Masters and Johnson, behavioural, psychotherapy and general counselling may all be applied when treating vaginismus. There are, however, three distinct schools of psychotherapy available in the United Kingdom:

Psychodynamic

A therapy in which a woman's psychological processes and forces are studied. This therapy is generally based upon the theories and techniques of Freud.

Behavioural

A therapy in which a woman's conditioning and learned

behaviour is studied.

Humanistic/Growth

A therapy (sometimes using group work) which involves working on the body as well as the mind with the emphasis on the spiritual side. These include Gestalt, Psychodrama, Encounter and Transpersonal.

Even within these three schools of therapy there may often be a mixture of one, two or sometimes all. However, for the majority of sufferers, psychodynamic and behavioural methods are the ones most commonly employed.

Apart from psychoanalysis with its rigid rules and guidelines, there really are no clearly defined boundaries separating one method from another. The most successful is ideally woman-orientated and therefore 'tailor made'. Perhaps the art of achieving a successful outcome is the ability to match the woman with the right therapy and therapist for her and her vaginismus. I don't believe there is only one definitive way to treat vaginismus; this can only be true if there is just one type of woman who has vaginismus. As one doctor says:

> Many roads lead to Rome, and we have to find the right treatment for every woman
> (Dr Anne Mathieson, Medical Hypnotherapist)

In fact, all practitioners agree that it's important to state that vaginismus can't be treated in any one specific way.

> What we need to get away from indicating to any woman is that there's a pattern she can go through. Every single woman will have got to this (vaginismus) in a very different way, so it can't be treated the same way either
> (Jill Curtis, Psychotherapist)

Another psychotherapist explains how she assesses each sufferer differently and how she adapts her method accordingly:

> There is no set way I work with a woman. With some, I decide very early on to try and encourage them to examine themselves, but with others I would not be working in the same way
> (Marianne Granö, Sexual Psychotherapist, Sweden)

What should determine the choice of treatment?

The suitability of a method will depend upon many factors, but probably the way a woman perceives vaginismus should be the ultimate determinant in deciding upon a treatment. If, for example, we see it as being a purely 'learned' or sexual problem, then the behavioural treatments which focus heavily on the symptom will be much more appropriate. However, if like me she sees vaginismus as not being separate from her but as part of a much deeper personality conflict, then the psychodynamic therapies which aim to give us insights into our psychology will probably be more suited.

This aspect is better explained by a practising psychologist who has experience and expertise in assessing patients:

> It's important diagnostically to distinguish between women who are fairly integrated about their sexuality and whose vaginismus often relates to very clear trauma they might have had experience of. There will be a lot of uncertainty or distress about the vagina and they just feel they can't relax enough to allow penetration to happen. This group is relatively simple to treat and typically women respond to behavioural programmes quite quickly. There is another group where the unconscious forces are much more in evidence with deep fears about what is going on inside them. This requires much more aware and sympathetic psychotherapy. Distinguishing between these two groups gives some clues as to what treatment method one is going to use, and the approach should be defined fairly early on
> (Dr Paul Brown, Consulting Clinical Psychologist)

Considering the diversity of women's personalities and experience, it is far better left open as to what therapy is most effective since this encourages seeing people as individuals. We should avoid trying to fit a woman to a treatment simply because it's voted the most 'successful' in treating vaginismus. Far better to try and fit the therapy to the woman.*

Before taking a look at what happens inside the therapists' consulting rooms, I would mention that the order in which each treatment is described is based upon the ease of availability and those methods most commonly employed in treating vaginismus. Their order, therefore, does not reflect in any way a hierarchy of preference or rates of success. For example, my own form of treatment is placed towards the end of this section simply because vaginismus is not very often treated by a psychoanalyst. Similarly, the treatments described, though based mainly upon women in heterosexual relationships relate equally to women in homosexual relationships.

Whilst I describe the many ways in which vaginismus may be treated by a professional, this does not necessarily imply that all the expertise is exclusively held by the specialist. I see the treatment as a process of sharing and learning rather than one which reinforces the woman as a patient with little power and no sense of her own expertise. In reality, it isn't just the 'expert' or treatment which counts, so much as our own contribution to the therapeutic partnership.

HOW TO READ THE TREATMENTS SECTION

Apart from 'Linda's Treatment' which is based upon my own experience of analytical psychotherapy, the names of all the sufferers in this section have been changed, and some of the 'case histories' are composites formed from the experiences of several different women. Each example is, nonetheless, a realistic portrayal of what actually happens inside the therapist's consulting room. Doctors and therapists are also quoted throughout this section, but their statements do not relate to the patients in any of my illustrated examples.

Although I describe each particular treatment, it naturally cannot represent the exact way in which it will be practised. This is because no two women are alike and no two therapists practise in the same way; each person will bring his or her

---

* Not all treatments are available on the NHS: see *Where are the Treatments Available*, p 193.

own instincts, style and creativity to their method. This means, for example, that you might find a psychosexual doctor practising much more psychodynamically, or a behavioural therapist who uses some analytic technique, or a sex therapist who rarely uses direct-counselling and relies almost solely on psychotherapy.

It is hoped that these examples convey some of the flavour of the therapeutic process. However, whatever method is used to illustrate a case study it can never truly convey the special and unique nature of the relationship which exists between one human being and another who has come to be healed by them. Described as a kind of psychological 'hand holding', it might be the doctor who becomes 'mother' giving us permission to enjoy sex, or the therapist who is the supportive teacher, or the analyst who conveys to a frightened woman that the alarming fantasies and fears that live inside her will neither destroy him nor her. For many of us, the therapeutic encounter may be the first time in our lives that we have someone on our side with whom we can go through such painful emotions.

Equally, my examples can never convey the pain, torment, frustration and sheer hard work that may often be experienced when trying to resolve vaginismus. Sometimes the lack of progress or emergence of painful feelings may become so unbearable that we may wish to discontinue treatment. Whatever treatment is finally undertaken it may often be a painful road, requiring enormous commitment from both the woman and the specialist, and it may also be a long road: a symptom which we have suffered from and lived with for a long period of our lives may well take a number of years to resolve. Therefore, each described method whilst only a few pages in length will have taken place over an extended period ranging from, say, three months to perhaps more than seven years.

Note:
I have chosen to refer to the doctor as a 'she' because the majority who treat vaginismus will be women. This is particularly relevant where cultural or religious factors dictate that *only* a woman doctor may carry out a vaginal examination.

PART I
ONE-TO-ONE THERAPY

This involves the woman working in a one-to-one relationship situation with her therapist. Sometimes her partner is also required to attend some, if not all, of the sessions.

BEHAVIOUR THERAPY

Behaviour therapy sees vaginismus not necessarily as the result of emotional conflicts, but as a learned or conditioned reflex which has been wrongly acquired as a way of coping with a certain stressful situation. In other words, vaginal spasm can be changed through unlearning and unconditioning. Although behavioural therapists are usually not concerned with the reasons why we have vaginismus, some psychologists have found they can successfully combine behavioural and psychodynamic approaches to our treatment.

The following are two behavioural techniques most commonly used by doctors and psychologists who treat vaginismus. However, it should be recognised that the techniques I describe cannot in themselves be seen as a 'therapy', they merely form part of a treatment programme.

SANDRA'S TREATMENT

Sandra was 23 and engaged to be married. Because she had never been able to insert tampons she believed her vagina was abnormally small and that a tough hymen was blocking the entrance. Consequently, she was convinced and frightened that penetration would damage her. Sandra was referred to a sex therapist by her general practitioner. The sessions took place once a week in an outpatients clinic of a large hospital.

Densitization

This is a gradual process whereby the therapist provides a graded series of experiences from the least to the most threatening. It is known as 'systematic desensitization' and proceeds mainly in two ways:

'in vitro' method:
(a process made to occur outside of our body in an artificial
environment)
Sandra was taught how to relax during a session and was
exposed to the feared situation in stages by being asked to
imagine all the steps of lovemaking through to penetration. In order to strengthen and speed up this process,
hypnosis may be used (see page 123). Once she could
tolerate the imagery in a session, Sandra was instructed to
reproduce this imagery at home with her partner until
intercourse could be attempted.
'in vivo' method:
(a process made to occur inside our body in a natural
environment)
This proceeded once Sandra felt relaxed enough to imagine
erotic and sexual situations and tolerate them without
panic. She learned how to pass a finger into her vagina and
was given glass objects (Hegar dilators) to take home and
insert gently into her vagina. The real purpose of the
dilators was not to enlarge Sandra's vagina – since this is
rarely the reason for vaginismus – but to convince her that
her vaginismus had been corrected and to give her
confidence. The dilators became larger and more penile in
size as the 'in vivo' treatment progressed.

Confronting the worst fear

The therapist explained that as part of Sandra's treatment,
and with her consent, she would confront her with the
most feared situation she could imagine without providing her with an opportunity to escape from her feelings.
This, the therapist explained, is called 'flooding'.

When Sandra became used to this process and could
'stay with' her fears, her phobic response (spasm) was
eventually extinguished. The theory is that once Sandra
was able to tolerate her worst fantasy, which was her
unconscious expectation of damage, Sandra would be able
to tolerate intercourse. The therapist also taught her
relaxation techniques to help her during this process.

The behavioural techniques of 'in vitro' and 'in vivo'
desensitization combined with the 'flooding' method were

used by Sandra's therapist so that once Sandra was able to insert the largest dilator and her phobia of penetration had been alleviated, she and her lover were encouraged to attempt intercourse. These techniques are particularly useful in treating vaginismus where the specific fear or phobia of penetration can impede and complicate treatment. Accordingly, some therapists may desensitize a woman prior to her commencing sexual therapy (described next).

SEX THERAPY (ALSO KNOWN AS INTERVENTION BEHAVIOUR MODIFICATION)

A form of behaviour therapy specifically to treat sexual problems was developed in the late 1950s by Americans Dr William Masters, an obstetrician, and Virginia Johnson, his researcher. Masters and Johnson believe vaginismus can be overcome in a rapid manner through intensive re-education as opposed to individual, probing and lengthy therapy which explores the deeper emotional conflicts. The techniques described form the main feature of most sex therapies, distinguishing it from psychotherapy and psychoanalysis. This is a very popular form of treatment and is used by clinical psychologists both in the NHS and private sector, as well as counsellors in the Marriage Guidance Council who have undergone sexual therapy training. Although described in stages, nothing can be expected to run to a set pattern or rigid timetable. As Alison Clegg explains:

> We have an open contract and always move at the client's pace. Although we have a basic programme we don't just process people through it. Each behavioural programme is tailor-made for each client-couple and takes account of their particular unique needs
> (Alison Clegg, Sex Therapy Training Officer, National Marriage Guidance Council)

Although a modified, much less intensive version of the original is practised in the U.K., the Masters and Johnson approach is better described in its entirety. Therefore, our story takes place across the Atlantic.

AMY & ROB'S TREATMENT

Amy (27) and Rob (29) live in an apartment in St Louis, Missouri. They have been married for three years but because of Amy's vaginismus have not been able to consummate their marriage. Amy imagined her vagina to be too small to accommodate Rob, and this led to her terror of being penetrated for fear she might be 'ripped apart'.

Amy felt sure she was the only woman who had this problem but through a magazine article came across the work of Masters and Johnson. She then asked her family doctor if he would refer her for treatment.

The couple as patient

Amy and Rob's doctor told them that Rob would have to be part of the therapy since Masters and Johnson never see vaginismus only as the woman's problem, but rather as a couple's joint difficulty. Accordingly, they were treated together ('conjoint therapy') and not individually.

> Masters and Johnson said some simple but revolutionary things like 'Sex tends to happen between two people' which we'd never observed before. Typically we would see only one person, not the couple, with a sexual difficulty
> (Dr Paul Brown, Consulting Clinical Psychologist)

Strict selection of patients

Their doctor explained to Amy and Rob that because of the rule in assessing suitability of couples they would not be accepted into the programme unless he, a psychologist or a social worker referred them.

Intensive treatment

Masters and Johnson believe that if sex is exposed to daily consideration, then stimulation elevates rapidly. Amy and Rob's therapy was therefore part of an intensive two-week residential daily format. They were required to check into an hotel and were isolated from the demands of everyday life with little or no outside pressures or distractions. This allowed for full concentration on resolving Amy's vaginismus.

> There is no intensive everyday treatment carried out in the U.K. but we have transferred Masters and Johnson's work into hospital outpatient departments (Dr Paul Brown, Consulting Clinical Psychologist)

The intensity of treatment is also considered important by Dr Cole:

> Ideally, I usually see women at weekly intervals. If you leave it too long then the motivation will drop
> (Dr Martin Cole, Sex Therapist)

Therapists work in pairs

Amy and Rob learned that Masters and Johnson prefer to have a male therapist working with a female (called 'co-therapists') as opposed to either of them working alone. The object of a same-sex therapist was for Amy to have 'a friend on her side' representing her in the joint sessions.

> Masters and Johnson co-therapists act in very prescribed ways and this kind of method has never been adopted in the U.K. For instance, the man never talks to the woman patient and she never talks to him so the sex barriers are never broken between therapist and patient in discussion. I prefer co-therapy because I think a woman therapist is immensely reassuring, but most people in the U.K. work in single therapy (Dr Paul Brown, Consulting Clinical Psychologist)

Indepth interview about family history

To ensure the suitability and success of Amy and Rob's treatment, careful separate assessments were made to ascertain whether Amy's vaginismus was primarily learned or psychological, and whether Rob had any impotency problems. If deeper roots had been suspected, then counselling would have been suggested in order to uncover any conflicts which might have hindered the progress of the behavioural methods.

> If the vaginismus is a deeper problem then one uses whatever counselling or psychotherapeutic strategy one feels is appropriate to get to the root of the problem
> (Dr Paul Brown, Consulting Clinical Psychologist)

Surrogate partners

Masters and Johnson introduced the use of surrogates into their programme in 1959. A surrogate is a lover provided by the co-therapists for people without partners. Some women may feel quite shocked, and others quite excited, at the prospect of making love with a stranger. Perhaps surrogates do have a place in sex therapy, but I have some reservations. In the United Kingdom surrogates are currently only used in one centre in the Midlands. Media sensationalism, legal difficulties and, more recently, AIDS, all inhibit the use of surrogates elsewhere:

> If a woman doesn't have a partner we would suggest the use of a surrogate, given her consent and understanding of what is involved. This has been the difference between no treatment at all for vaginismus, and treatment
> (Dr Martin Cole, Sex Therapist)

Re-education about the vagina and sex

The existence of Amy's spasm was demonstrated to her and Rob, firstly by showing them diagrams of the involuntary reflex action (a revelation to them both) and then a doctor attempted to perform a vaginal examination by introducing one finger into Amy's vagina in the presence of Rob.

> I make sure the woman knows her anatomy by teaching her about it, by getting her to read books. I help her understand the pelvic anatomy so that she knows the musculature
> (Dr Paul Brown, Consulting Clinical Psychologist)

Psycho-education is critical. I simply explain the normality of the experience of intercourse, explaining that the muscles are not there to close her vagina, that they're there to open it. We also use video films showing women inserting dilators so she can actually see how the vagina opens up
(Dr Martin Cole, Sex Therapist)

Kegel exercises, relaxation and the use of fantasy

Vaginal exercises originally devised by a Dr Kegel are to help women restore muscle tone after childbirth since it is believed that poor muscle tone may impair sexual enjoyment. Amy was instructed to contract and release a muscle in her vagina ('Pubococcygeus' – PC for short) as if she was trying to stop the flow of urine. This demonstrated to Amy that she indeed had control over her vagina. The exercises also increased awareness of Amy's feelings, and with the focus on pleasant and new sensations she was encouraged to enjoy sexual fantasies. The aim was to help reduce anxiety, and associate pleasure (not the conditioned fear of pain) with penetration.

I would get her into a method of relaxing. It might simply be warm baths, or I might teach her relaxation or use hypnosis to induce relaxation
(Dr Paul Brown, Consulting Clinical Psychologist)

I think it's important that the woman be able to imagine herself having intercourse and being aroused
(Dr Martin Cole, Sex Therapist)

Throughout the entire programme, Amy was encouraged to report on her feelings and fantasies that emerged either during or after a particular exercise or task was carried out.

Desensitization

Using in vitro and in vivo methods of desensitization (as in Sandra's treatment), dilators of graduating size were demonstrated and given to Amy, and she and Rob were instructed to insert them into Amy's vagina at home. After they could be introduced successfully without anxiety, Amy was encouraged to retain the largest dilator inside her vagina for several hours each night to accustom her to the feeling.

> Rather than use dilators (because it introduces a foreign object) I prefer her to use her fingers and would suggest she explores the outer entrance to the vagina. Once she begins to feel safer and more skilful, she can go on from one finger to two. Once she has done this I would begin to teach her partner the same skills of finger insertion. It's typical that after three-finger insertion a woman begins to be interested in introducing an erection
> (Dr Paul Brown, Consulting Clinical Psychologist)

As Dr Brown explained, he does not use dilators, and many other therapists follow the practice of encouraging the woman to accept her or her partner's finger(s) rather than a foreign object. However, sometimes there may be a good reason why a dilator is suggested. Alison Clegg explains:

> We don't like the word dilator because it suggests that the vagina is too small and has to be stretched. We call them 'vaginal trainers'. The only circumstances in which we would introduce them is when the woman is unable to make the transition from fingers to penis. If she despairs at this point we can reassure her and offer her the trainers as another resource
> (Alison Clegg, Sex Therapy Training Officer, National Marriage Guidance Council)

Sensate Focusing

Simultaneous to the accomplishment of the other techniques, Amy and Rob were given homework assignments in the form of erotic tasks to be performed in private. This is called 'sensate focusing' whereby the focus of sexual activity is removed from penetration by banning intercourse, and pleasure centres around stroking, kissing, massage and caressing with the emphasis on the motto 'sex is fun'. The anxiety and stress which so often surrounds vaginismus may ultimately remove enjoyment from lovemaking, so these tasks, instead of being goal orientated, were designed to encourage Amy and Rob to abandon themselves to sensations rather than strive for penetration. Only when they felt ready to embark upon intercourse were they encouraged to do so. This is generally after the woman is able to insert the trainers herself.

> We call the stage before intercourse the 'quiet vagina' and suggest the partner lies on his back whilst she gets into the female superior position. In this way she feels more in control and less anxious that he will overpower her
> (Alison Clegg, Sex Therapy Training Officer, National Marriage Guidance Council)

Amy was encouraged to attempt penetration by kneeling astride Rob and lowering herself onto his penis which he kept still. In this way, Amy was using Rob's penis as a trainer. It was suggested that Rob shouldn't thrust into Amy, but allow her the opportunity to experience the sensations that the presence of his penis inside her evoked. Amy was asked in the following session how it had made her feel to have Rob inside her, and Rob was asked how it had felt for him. Once penetration occurred in this way, then sexual intercourse could be attempted in any position they chose, with the encouragement that Amy makes the thrusting movements herself.

> I wouldn't regard the treatment of vaginismus as being complete simply because the woman can tolerate penetration. There is a big difference between tolerating penetration and being capable and skilful at making love. Being sexually competent is not just being able to relax enough to be fertilized; these days it's about appreciating one's sexuality
> (Dr Paul Brown, Consulting Clinical Psychologist)

DOCTOR PSYCHOSEXUAL COUNSELLING

Psychosexual medicine is a form of therapy commonly

practised in the U.K. and started in 1958 under the Family Planning Association. It is concerned with understanding how unconscious emotional factors interfere with our sexual function and enjoyment. The work of London's Institute of Psychosexual Medicine is known for its concentration on the doctor-patient relationship, aiming to enhance the doctor's sensitivity to what is going on in herself and in us, both consciously and unconsciously, when we are together. This demands a kind of listening which is different from the traditional medical approach of history-taking. Since many of us find it difficult to reveal, even to a doctor, that we have vaginismus, it will be important for the doctor to discover an ability to listen to things that are barely said and begin listening to the same kind of language in herself.[1]

TINA'S TREATMENT

Tina (26) has been married for two years. She had always dreaded penetration and recalled hearing at school that first-time sex was always painful. Because Tina felt so shy and embarrassed that she hadn't had intercourse she felt unable to consult her general practitioner. Instead she made an appointment with a family planning clinic on the pretext of wanting to go on the Pill. The doctor Tina saw was a member of the Institute and she endeavoured to help Tina discover for herself the nature of the block that prevented her from engaging in and enjoying intercourse.

The doctor's awareness and sensitivity to the woman

The doctor's training encouraged her to become sensitive to what Tina transmitted. When the doctor felt something this feeling was not acted upon but examined and understood as an indication of some underlying conflict in Tina.

> I hold an unstructured interview. In fact, I don't speak but wait for her to, so that she talks about the things that are on her mind and I encourage her to say more. I try and notice what is going on in the interaction between me and the patient, and I try to understand it. Is she treating me like a mother, or a teacher or asking

for tips and help? Those are the kinds of clues which give me an idea as to what's going on and I can perhaps put it back to her so that she gets a better understanding of herself
(Dr Robina Thexton, Member, Inst. Psychosexual Medicine)

Another doctor explains how the body can 'speak' for a woman:

What you get with some women who have vaginismus is the same thing in a consultation that you get within her body, and that is she has an extreme difficulty in talking
(Dr Katharine Draper, Member, Inst. Psychosexual Medicine)

Therapeutic use of vaginal examination

Attention was focused on Tina's genital difficulty, and interpretations were offered at that level mostly. Although some counselling was used, the doctor was primarily concerned with Tina's body and, unlike psychotherapists and psychoanalysts, was prepared to examine Tina's vagina. The examination was made not only to check pelvic normality, but also to create a situation in which Tina's reactions could be observed, and fears and fantasies discussed. Typically, psychosexual treatment involves the doctor examining and talking to a woman at the same time. This approach is called psychosomatic, because Tina's mind (psyche) as well as body (soma) are examined together.

All along the line I am thinking is it an appropriate moment to examine this patient and if it isn't why isn't it? Sensitive handling of the genital examination is a very important part. The examination itself is a very vital time when we encourage her to talk about her feelings about her body, why is it tight, what is the pain? Our method is aimed at understanding what happens during this examination when the woman reveals feelings about her body
(Dr Robina Thexton, Member. Inst. Psychosexual

Medicine)

But it isn't just the actual examination which can give clues; as one doctor points out, she also observes the way a woman prepares herself for the examination:

> It's also significant how she gets on the couch. All the time the women are showing you (these) things and I can see what she is saying about her sexuality
> (Dr Katharine Draper, Member. Inst. Psychosexual Medicine)

Encouragement to express fantasies and fears

A central aspect of Tina's treatment was the encouragement and invitation for her to discuss her fantasies whilst being vaginally examined. This sought to integrate the physical examination with a thorough psychological examination of Tina's emotions and imaginings, centred on her vagina and its function. It was felt that fearful, unrealistic fantasies would cease being such strong barriers against intercourse once expressed, and examined and discussed openly.[2] Tina was then better able to recognise them as unrealistic and thereby ceased to be so inhibited by them.

> I take it little by little and just go on and on, in very short steps. Once we begin to make a little progress I say: look, I've slipped a finger in, what about you trying? But all the time thinking about what we are doing, not just doing it like dilators and making it bigger but trying in that way to reach her ideas. Sometimes when they are on the couch women will produce their ideas and usually we can reach them
> (Dr Katharine Draper, Member, Inst. Psychosexual Medicine)

NURSE PSYCHOSEXUAL COUNSELLING

As a result of three DHSS pilot studies in 1974, it was recognised that nurses play a very important role in this field. The English National Board Course 985 trains nurses in understanding the principles of psychosexual counselling. Although she will not have necessarily undertaken a training in psychotherapy, nurses requesting this training are from a variety of specialties. Some will have had extensive experience in family planning work, and this work will have involved her in understanding, communicating and examining women's bodies. The combination of gynaecological knowledge and communication skills give a Nurse-Therapist particular expertise in being able to treat vaginismus. A woman with vaginismus may either be seen by a doctor or a nurse in a clinic because caseloads tend to be shared by all practitioners. Although the methods of treatment by a doctor or nurse are similar, there will always be variations, just as two people of the same profession do not practise in exactly the same way. Nurses with this special training, together with a recognised counselling training, are called Nurse Psychosexual Counsellors.

LOUISE'S TREATMENT

Louise is 24 and has been married for 18 months. She came to the family planning clinic initially asking for infertility help. She was very tearful, but eventually the nurse was able to elicit from Louise that the reason why she could not get pregnant was because she and her husband were unable to have intercourse. Louise explained how she had always been terrified of examining her vagina (which she described as 'small, slimy and dark') and any attempt her husband made to penetrate ended in tears and pain because her vagina clamped tightly shut.

Talking, listening and examining

The nurse explained to Louise that initially she would like to see her and her husband together. Louise and her partner were then seen individually and the nurse described the treatment to them. Part of this assessment involved the nurse listening and trying to understand what Louise was saying.

> The women have great difficulty in explaining what is wrong with them, thinking they are the only ones

with this particular problem. I'm not always able to examine during the first consultation, but when the woman is in that particular position on the couch we can eliminate quite a lot of fears, and she begins to tell quite a few things
(Barbara Lamb, Nurse Psychosexual Counsellor)

Counselling plus sensate-focusing

Louise told the nurse she felt a great a sense of relief at being able to talk about and share her anxieties with somebody who was understanding and did not laugh at her. The nurse used her skills individually to suit each woman she saw. She combined looking at Louise's psychological problems with sensate focus exercises to remove the pressure from penetration (as in Amy's treatment).

I talk a lot about a woman's feelings, what are her expectations, how long has she had vaginismus. Then maybe we will do some exploration on the first visit. I think what makes my treatment successful is possibly women find it easier to relate to a nurse than a doctor. They feel very much on the same level as me
(Barbara Lamb, Nurse Psychosexual Counsellor)

Helping a woman to accept and own her vagina

The nurse felt she could work successfully with Louise since she saw the vaginismus as more to do with the need for Louise to come to terms with her own body, as opposed to something deeply psychological. In some family planning clinics there may be a psychiatrist working alongside psychosexual doctors and nurse therapists. Whilst a psychiatrist treats the psychological aspects of vaginismus, he will not examine her. The nurse, however, was able to treat Louise's vaginismus on a practical level without psychiatric intervention. She offered Louise self-exploration techniques to help understand her vagina more.

I make it quite simple; I look at and treat much more

the physical part rather than the mental side of vaginismus. But also one needs to understand WHY a woman feels she can't consummate her relationship. I do believe a woman has got to learn to examine her own body, know what vaginismus is, know that it's a muscular spasm. Knowing what she is doing when penetration takes place and how to avoid this happening
(Barbara Lamb, Nurse Psychosexual Counsellor)

Guidance & Self-Help

After several sessions the nurse was able to teach Louise how to pass one, two and three fingers painlessly into Louise's vagina (as in Sandra, Amy and Ellen's treatments). Dilators were not used as the nurse found women preferred to insert either fingers or the contraceptive cap. She observed that women found the cap more acceptable as it gently and naturally expands inside the vagina as it enters.

> I don't promise success overnight and explain that we have to work through it together. The couple make it work, but as the counsellor I see myself as their 'referee' to guide them through it. When the woman is ready to make love I usually suggest the female superior position so that she is in control
> (Barbara Lamb, Nurse Psychosexual Counsellor)

COMBINED BEHAVIOURAL & PSYCHODYNAMIC SEX THERAPY

In the field of psychosexual medicine, information and techniques are constantly evolving and improving both through large organisations of medical bodies and individual practitioners. To reflect this, in the 1970s a combination of behavioural and psychodynamic methods was introduced in the USA by Dr. Helen Singer Kaplan, a professor of psychiatry. Her treatment (known as the 'New Sex Therapy') is a kind of marriage between behavioural and psychodynamic techniques. Kaplan's method rejects the Freudian view that cites unconscious conflicts always as being the cause of vaginismus, and focuses on the present rather than the past. It goes one step further than Masters and Johnson because it not only uses desensitization techniques, but also attempts to make our unconscious more conscious and so reduce our phobia rapidly. This combined approach aims to deal with the psychological issues as they crop up, but not in anything like the depth of, say, psychotherapy or psychoanalysis. It may, however, help us to gain simple insights into our childhood or crucial early experiences which may have been contributing factors in the causes of vaginismus.

As with the Masters and Johnson therapy, this treatment originated in the USA, though it has since been adopted by doctors in the U.K.

ELLEN'S TREATMENT

Ellen is 35 and shares an apartment with two girlfriends in Manhattan, New York. After a five-year marriage in which she was unable to engage in intercourse, she and her husband separated one year ago. Ellen always had a fearful expectation that penetration would cause her pain and bleeding, and was referred for treatment by a psychiatrist.

Dealing with the immediate cause of spasm

Using behavioural methods the doctor focused initially on the 'immediate' causes of Ellen's vaginismus (cited as poor relationships, ignorance and anxiety about sex or perform- ance). If progress was not being made then using psychodynamic methods the doctor would have directed her attention to the 'remote' causes (responsible for the beginnings of Ellen's spasm and usually occurring during early development or after a trauma).

This may often involve the doctor actually by-passing the exploration of deeper origins of vaginismus. Doctors (like Ellen's) who practise this method tend to believe that this exploration is simply not needed to enable them to resolve the symptom.

Ellen was so fearful of the internal examination that she found it difficult to get onto the examination couch: for some women it can take them a large part of the session. Once there, Ellen, found it impossible even to open her legs. They just didn't seem to come under her control. The first step, therefore, was to help Ellen learn how to relax her thigh muscles to allow the doctor access to her vulva and then eventually for the doctor to simply place one finger at the entrance of the vagina.

The marriage between the behavioural and psychodynamic approach meant that Ellen's doctor could use physical techniques to help desensitize Ellen's conditioned response to being penetrated. Glass dilators were not used (as in Sandra's and Amy's treatments). Instead, the doctor began with her finger and then progressed on to 'trainers'. Kegel exercises were also taught (as with Amy) to relax Ellen's vaginal muscles and give her awareness of her own self-control and bodily sensations.

For the doctor, spasm may feel like trying to put a finger through the centre of the palm of a hand, so Ellen's doctor pressed ever so slightly, without pushing her finger in. At this stage she began to teach Ellen how to tighten and loosen her vaginal muscles, never pushing her finger in against tight muscles but instead making it clear that it was only when Ellen relaxed her muscles that her finger would go on. In this way, Ellen was letting in the doctor, not the doctor pushing her finger in.

All the while, Ellen's doctor was helping her explore her feelings at each stage of the examination. When the doctor's finger was at the entrance of Ellen's vagina Ellen revealed feelings of terror, fear of being ripped apart, and a devastating destruction of some kind . . . almost like an annihilation. These feelings were discussed so that Ellen was finally helped to understand them.

Intercourse was not attempted until Ellen could insert a 'trainer' into her vagina without fear or pain. Since many women with vaginismus harbour a distorted and very negative image about their bodies, with the help of the doctor Ellen learned the facts about her genital area.

Deeper exploration only when necessary

This method was primarily limited to relief of Ellen's

vaginismus without exploring its origins, and as such its relief had to override any other factors. The deeper ('remote') causes were dealt with only when they presented an obstacle to consummation.

When a difficulty did emerge, such as Ellen repeatedly not being able to allow the doctor's finger to enter her vagina, it was then that Ellen's doctor began to explore, interpret and analyse her resistance. If there had been deeper conflicts making Ellen's vaginismus harder to overcome with this approach, this may have indicated a referral for individual psychotherapy.

WHO BENEFITS MOST FROM THE BEHAVIOURAL, PSYCHOSEXUAL & SEX THERAPIES?

If a woman, although apprehensive, is able to tolerate a one finger examination without trauma then this process is reassuring and can be seen as the first step taken in the therapeutic reversal of an involuntary spasm.[3] Likewise, if she sees vaginismus as being a purely sexual difficulty, seeks rapid insights without the desire for deeper changes, is keenly motivated and can recognise the link between mind and body, she may be more suited to the directive methods. However, behavioural techniques are generally employed only when the phobia of penetration is secondary to the vaginismus.

Behaviour therapy works on the assumption that a psychologically-rooted spasm can be consciously separated and treated externally with direct instructions and exercises. Whilst this treatment might well suit the woman who sees vaginismus purely as a sexual difficulty, the woman who cannot separate the vaginismus from her other conflicts may not respond so well. If the prospect of a vaginal examination fills us with dread and horror, if we suffer from severe problems of needing to have power over and control over the doctor, or if we are phobic about being touched vaginally, then the physical methods employed by these treatments should not be undertaken. Any severe anxieties continuing to prevent an examination should be taken as an indicator that we need to go deeper into the underlying conflicts to bring about resolution of vaginismus.

> If the emotional block is so deep-seated then possibly nobody is going to get to it unless the woman receives a full psychoanalysis. I would try and refer her on after an interval. Sometimes the woman gets desperately despairing about the lack of movement and she drops out of treatment. Maybe her need to stay in control of her body, the muscle and her life is so strong, but I always hope to have pointed that out to her before we part. If she doesn't turn up for treatment than I write a letter about it so that we try and get it out in the open
> (Dr. Robina Thexton, Member, Inst. Psychosexual Medicine)

I share Masters and Johnson's view that it is unnecessarily brutal for a woman to be placed in a situation which might severely traumatize her. If an internal can only be accomplished by employing force, then clearly this approach must be decried. Nothing is accomplished in such a way and the resultant trauma can make vaginismus even more difficult to treat.[4]

HYPNOTHERAPY

As with the desensitization techniques in Sandra's treatment, hypnosis should not be viewed as a complete therapy for vaginismus when used on its own. Rather, it is generally used in addition to a doctor's or therapist's other skills in the treatment of vaginismus.

It was a frenchman, Anton Mesmer (1734–1815) who discovered a technique which claimed to produce remarkable changes in behaviour. Hypnosis involves suggestion by the hypnotist to produce in his patient an altered state of consciousness combined to bring about a change in behaviour. This was the original technique used by psychoanalysts (notably Freud) in the treatment of emotional problems. Put simply, hypnotherapy used solely on its own is trying to do what behavioural therapy does, and that is change a learned response (spasm) through positive suggestion. The difference is that in hypnosis the suggestion is received in a 'trance' state. If my psychoanalyst had used hypnosis (as some do) it would have been as an aid to further assist in the uncovering of repressed material. However, behavioural therapists who use hypnosis (as in Sandra's treatment) do so strictly for the purpose of direct behaviour modification or to induce relaxation.

I would always recommend that hypnosis only be sought from a doctor, clinical psychologist, or qualified psychotherapist/analyst.

JACKIE'S TREATMENT

Jackie (22) has been married for one year. Because she fears being torn apart during penetration she has never been able to insert tampons or allow intercourse. Jackie also has a phobia about being vaginally examined. Her GP referred her to a doctor who uses hypnosis as an adjunct to her psychosexual skills. The following takes place over a period of six sessions, each lasting approximately two hours.

Positive conditioning

In common with other psychosomatic conditions, Jackie's vaginismus was seen by the doctor to be the result of poor conditioning deriving from an unconscious block which governs Jackie's reflexes. Under hypnosis, the doctor believed the spasm could be resolved by positive subconscious reconditioning to end the reflex response. If an unresolved emotional conflict (real or imagined) has had to be repressed, it usually translates itself into a self-punishing response expressed involuntarily through the body – in this case, Jackie's vagina. What reconditioning aims to do is allow Jackie to rearrange the stimulus-response cues which produce the vaginismus.

The value of hypnotherapy

- Hypnosis allowed for the doctor to explore Jackie's underlying unconscious reasons for her vaginismus.

  Not every medical hypnotist uses the analytic exploratory side. Quite a lot will be using hypnosis more as a

reprogramming with positive suggestions on the behavioural side, but in the hypnotic trance state where the suggestions are more readily accepted
(Dr Anne Mathieson, Medical Hypnotherapist)

– Jackie found hypnosis was in itself relaxing and calming. She had inevitably become very tense because of the vaginismus and was able to learn how to induce relaxation in herself.

– In the hypnotic state Jackie was more responsive to positive suggestions than when she was wide awake.

It's not magic. You can't tell a woman, as our fantasies would tell us, to go away, do this, that or the other, but repeated suggestions in the trance state are more readily accepted. It can be used to suggest a change of attitude and substitute a new way of responding for old
(Dr Anne Mathieson, Medical Hypnotherapist)

– The doctor made general positive suggestions about Jackie's specialness and abilities in order to strengthen Jackie's ego.

Inducing the hypnotic state

One definition of the hypnotic trance is that it's a state in which one has shifted one's viewpoint from the rational logical thought processes of the left frontal lobe of the brain to the more imaginative intuitive functioning of the right frontal lobe.
(Dr Anne Mathieson, Medical Hypnotherapist)

The hypnotist's method is probably already familiar to many of us from TV, films or on the stage. However, in reality it is a far more scientific and considered process. The relaxed sensory state ('trance') was induced in Jackie in three phases, although as with any treatment methods of induction may be many and varied:

PHASE ONE:
Eye fixation: The doctor asked Jackie to focus on a particular object in her room or to close her eyes and relax. During induction, Jackie's attention was fixed by concentrating on the sensation of her closed eyelids.

PHASE TWO:
Body and mental relaxation: Jackie's doctor asked her to let her mind go along and tune in to what she was saying and suggesting to her. She asked her not to try too hard to concentrate on her every word or else Jackie might become tense and wide awake.

> I explain this to the patient as letting her busy-planning-organising part of her mind free-wheel and slip into neutral gear
> (Dr Anne Mathieson, Medical Hypnotherapist)

PHASE THREE:
Journey into childhood: Jackie's doctor aimed to find the roots of the vaginismus and her accompanying anxieties and fears. When Jackie was reasonably hypnotized the doctor counted down the years telling Jackie that the index finger of her right hand would lift or flicker spontaneously at every year in her life where her unconscious mind was aware of some important root source of fear and anxiety in relation to her vagina. These years were then explored in turn. The doctor also asked questions directly to Jackie's unconscious mind telling her that her right hand would lift spontaneously if the answer from the unconscious mind was 'yes' and the left hand would lift for 'no'. Once the causes of spasm could be traced and identified (not always possible or necessary) then the doctor introduced some positive suggestions.

> Once one has cleared the trouble then it's at this point that I might say: look, now you can see why your personal 'computer' was wrongly programmed and we must now put in a nice positive feeling if you believe this part of your body is damaged
> (Dr Anne Mathieson, Medical Hypnotherapist)

Contrary to popular belief, at no time during the trance did Jackie receive the command: 'When you wake up you won't have vaginismus'.

> It's not appropriate to tell somebody she won't do
> something when she still has an unconscious reason
> for doing it, particularly where there might be a very
> profound unconscious reason for the spasm. You are
> then going to set up a great deal of inner conflict
> which isn't going to be helpful to the endeavour at all
> (Dr Anne Mathieson, Medical Hypnotherapist)

Suggestions to disassociate pain from intercourse

The sensations of heaviness, warmth and tingling were
induced in Jackie by the doctor, and in this relaxed sensory
state she was open to the associative suggestions she
would be given. These were aimed at inducing in her an
acceptance of the new ways of interpreting sensations.
Since Jackie was acutely phobic about anything entering
her, she was encouraged to react to penetration in the
context of the non-threatening, painless, warm and
pleasant sensations she was experiencing whilst in the
trance.

> The way I generally put it is to say she will find she has
> all the confidence in the world and it may well be
> much sooner than she would have expected it. I also
> make general suggestions that she will feel more
> confident and happy about her body, particularly
> with the sexual part of it
> (Dr Anne Mathieson, Medical Hypnotherapist)

When this new sensation was sufficiently implanted and
Jackie was taken out of trance, her reaction to penetration
was without the usual phobia and fear. However, since
Jackie couldn't live in a permanent hypnotic state, nor
carry the doctor around with her, she was taught to use the
technique of 'auto-suggestion'. This is a kind of Do-It-
Yourself-Relaxation which enables her to summon up in
her mind the pleasant sensations experienced in hypnosis
if ever she feels fearful and anxious about a situation.

Freud and Hypnosis

The popular image of the hypnotist as a theatrical

performer with swaying watch in reality bears no similarity to the very serious and committed work of many practitioners. Much of the scepticism and hostility directed towards hypnosis may have been the result of Freud's and the psychoanalytic movement's rejection of the method. It should be explained that in Freud's time hypnosis was still in its infancy and the understanding of the process was limited. Many analysts feared that a hypnotist 'did' something to the patient, or brainwashed them, and they didn't like the notion that doctors were planting ideas into peoples' minds or manipulating them. For a while, Freud experimented with hypnotic suggestion but soon found it to be an imperfect technique, acting uncertainly and often not at all. He eventually abandoned the use of suggestion and replaced it with a new method which became known as 'free association' (see *Linda's Treatment*). Although hypnosis doesn't render a person unconscious, Freud concluded that it could never be as valuable as his method; in analysis patients make decisions and connections in full consciousness, confronting in total awareness the hidden conflicts behind their problems. Accordingly, the majority of psychoanalysts tend to favour 'free association' believing it to be a more effective way of reaching a person's unconscious.

Answering the critics

Because hypnosis is often misunderstood, I asked Dr Mathieson if she could clarify some specific matters with particular regard to the treatment of vaginismus. To avoid any misinterpretation, Dr Mathieson's answers are directly quoted:

Q: When used purely as behaviour modification, does hypnosis work within narrow bounds since much detail of my life is excluded?

A: I always take a very full case history before I proceed with any treatment

Q: For hypnosis to be effective, is repression of my deeper conflicts necessary?

A: Whatever one does with hypnosis, it's collaboration between patient and doctor and so long as one has an open understanding between each other, there's no need for repression of any kind

Q: If I request hypnosis to overcome vaginismus, might I be demonstrating a wish to have it magically hypnotized away by someone else, reflecting an unwillingness to take responsibility for touching my body and being active in the healing process?

A: A woman may well be expressing this wish, but as far as the way I work is concerned she will discover that that's not the way we are going to get there

Q: Does making problems 'vanish' as if in a disappearing act suggest a by-passing of my unconscious?

A: On the contrary, I think hypnosis puts one in touch with the unconscious, and I don't believe one can override the unconscious with simple positive suggestions

Q: Are the results of hypnotherapy short-lived, limited, artificial and transient?

A: This would only be the case if one was using hypnosis purely to put in positive suggestions. What I aim to do is look at the underlying dynamics and any changes would be of real depth. However, if one is using hypnosis to persuade someone to do something they don't really want to do, like give up smoking, then there will be a very high failure rate

Q: Some of the most damaging criticisms are claims that hypnosis can't be proven. One American researcher says there is no evidence that hypnosis even exists.[5] Is this true?

A: One can prove certain things about the hypnotic state.

Body temperature drops and patients start to shiver. If one measures the basal-metabolic rate that has also dropped a bit. In addition, if one obtains electrical brain wave recordings in hypnotic trance they are different from both the waking and the sleeping state and closely akin to the meditation states

WHO BENEFITS MOST FROM HYPNOTHERAPY?

In 1953 a Select Committee set up by the British Medical Association studied the value of hypnosis. They concluded it was a useful tool of therapy to ease pain and fear in dental treatment and childbirth. In particular, they found hypnosis was most valuable in treating psychosomatic conditions. Since vaginismus is truly psychosomatic, hypnosis may have a part to play in the treatments of some sufferers.

> Hypnosis is an appropriate form of treating vaginismus because one can get down to the roots of what has gone wrong
> (Dr Anne Mathieson, Medical Hypnotherapist)

If, like Jackie, we are so irrationally frightened of a vaginal examination, then it may be that hypnosis can be used to deeply relax us and help us overcome this fear. On the surface, hypnosis might appeal mostly to the woman who is attracted to a method whereby she is passively led by a powerful, guiding 'parent', giving her commands. This, however, is not always the case:

> One might play it as the all-powerful doctor making suggestions, but I choose not to do this. The way that I work is that I believe the woman must be responsible for her own life and her own self and I am there to help her
> (Dr Anne Mathieson, Medical Hypnotherapist)

PSYCHOTHERAPY, PSYCHOANALYSIS & FEMINIST THERAPY

What separates the following three treatments from any other is their total reliance upon the relationship between patient and therapist. When I consult my general practitioner I will walk away with, hopefully, the right advice or prescription irrespective of whether he and I relate closely. The same would be true of the surgeon who may, in some instances, never have conversed with a patient, but nonetheless can perform a successful operation. Because an analyst/therapist doesn't dispense pills or examine us physically, the treatment is totally reliant upon relating. This is central to therapy because it's the love* and security which our therapist offers that can ultimately heal, strengthen and mature our personality.

Relating intimately and honestly is what makes psychotherapy the most powerful, yet paradoxically most difficult, of all methods. A doctor generally relies on medical and scientific knowledge, but therapy is carried out on the basis of therapists knowing themselves and us as people. A therapist is required to be emotionally perceptive and to work intuitively; he must identify with us in order to get to know us. We meet with him on an emotional, not intellectual, level, he being someone who has faced similar conflicts and understands himself. His understanding and knowledge don't just come simply from theories he's studied, but rather from his ability to identify and feel with and for his patient. Psychodynamic technique alone will not cure vaginismus; it is simply a way of investigating our unconscious processes, and whilst an essential part of therapy it isn't the healing factor. Change, growth and resolution come about as the direct result of a genuine loving relationship in which we're able to discover and receive new knowledge about ourselves because we feel cared for, known and understood.

The analyst Donald Winnicott likened the therapeutic relationship to that of mother and infant. Just as mother is free to use both the factual and personal knowledge she has in order to meet baby's needs, so too our therapist will use whatever intellectual knowledge his training has given him, but only in addition to, not in place of, his intimate and intuitive knowledge of us.

---

*The kind of love described here is akin to parental and known as 'agape'. This is distinct from 'eros' which is sexual love.

PSYCHOTHERAPY

The term psychotherapy basically describes a conversation between patient and therapist. This method is based upon psychoanalytic theory, but differs from traditional analysis in technique, depth, length of treatment and degree of personality change produced.

You may wish to opt for psychotherapy if:

- full scale psychoanalysis is financially out of the question.

- you do not live close to a large city where psychoanalysis is available.

- you feel your vaginismus can be resolved without the use of a technique aimed to bring about extensive and deep changes in your personality and functioning.

Psychotherapists generally base their work on Freudian concepts, combining this orientation with aspects of Jung, Klein, Gestalt and feminism (see *Jenny's Treatment*).

MAUREEN'S TREATMENT

Maureen (35) has been married for ten years, with two children aged six and two. Since the birth of her second child Maureen has been unable to allow penetration as her vagina goes into spasm ('secondary' vaginismus). She told her GP that she had intense pain during penetration, and described to him the traumatic delivery of her last baby involving many stitches. Maureen's GP examined her but could find no evidence of scarring nor any physical reason to account for the spasm. One of Maureen's friends had recently received successful therapy for a psychosomatic condition, and suggested this to Maureen. She then contacted a psychotherapist via an organisation. Their ethical requirement meant that any therapist treating vaginismus was required to be in contact with the general practitioner, so Maureen's doctor was asked to confirm a clinical diagnosis of vaginismus before psychotherapy began.

Modified psychoanalysis combining several techniques

In many ways, psychotherapy is a modified version of classical psychoanalysis. Maureen's therapist tended to be more directive and advisory, as opposed to the traditionally non-commital, aloof and distant analyst. Although Maureen wasn't required to lie down on a couch, some therapists do prefer its use as it can help their patients to focus introspectively. Maureen also had less frequent sessions than a patient in analysis, though again the frequency will be determined by a woman's individual needs; and her therapist tended to focus more on her current life problems, as opposed to her past.

> When I start I always focus on the present situation, then of course in these discussions we try to discover the reason for her fears. The history comes along with the discussion of how she copes with her sexuality (Marianne Granö, Sexual Psychotherapist, Sweden)

Maureen was listened to in a non-judgmental and accepting way, and the simple act of 'talking things out' provided a healing effect. It helped Maureen to release bottled-up anxieties that she had previously held in her unconscious. The holding-in of feelings was contributing to Maureen's pain during intercourse.

> I tend to pull back from the vaginismus and just say: let's get to know you. I explain the process to people that it's a bit like tipping a jigsaw puzzle on the table and then together trying to see what picture we can get, and the vaginismus would be part of that (Jill Curtis, Psychotherapist)

Understanding the reasons behind the vaginismus

Maureen's therapy was more concerned with her external life and environment, as opposed to her inner and unconscious worlds, although some therapists work much like a psychoanalyst in this respect. Maureen's therapy aimed to resolve her vaginismus but also gave support to wider objectives, such as improving her life in general.

Maureen's therapist didn't treat the vaginismus in

isolation from other conflicts in Maureen's life, connecting it with the marital crisis she and her partner had been experiencing since the birth of their last baby. Nor was the vaginismus treated directly by examination, re-education or dilatation (as with Amy, Ellen, Sandra and Louise). The emphasis was on resolving Maureen's deeper conflicts, helping her to make sense of and see some sort of reason behind the muscle spasm.

> I think what makes psychotherapy an appropriate treatment for vaginismus is because you are really going to the roots of something. It takes time, patience and understanding to get to the root of why this particular woman has developed this particular difficulty. You've got to work at it on a conscious level and also on an unconscious level because that's where the spasm is coming from
> (Jill Curtis, Psychotherapist)

WHO BENEFITS MOST FROM PSYCHOTHERAPY?

Any woman unable to tolerate the prospect of vaginal examination or who doesn't feel vaginismus is simply a sexual problem, might find the 'talking cure' more suitable. However, we would have to be prepared to engage in the exploration of the underlying causes in ways not required of Sandra, Amy, Ellen and Louise. Likewise, a woman who is unable to cope with the more distanced approach of psychoanalysis, who may find it difficult to tolerate having feelings stirred up by deeper probing, or who may be isolated with little outside support might benefit more from this type of method. This is because psychotherapy is generally less exploratory and more overtly supportive than psychoanalysis.

ANALYTICAL PSYCHOTHERAPY, FREUDIAN & JUNGIAN PSYCHOANALYSIS

As a mode of therapy, psychoanalysis was developed in the late 1890s by Sigmund Freud, a Viennese psychiatrist, and may be considered the prototype of all psychotherapies. To simplify, psychoanalysis consists of two people (analyst and analysand) meeting in order to understand what is going on in the unconscious of one of them. This method differs from most other treatments for vaginismus as it isn't symptom-led.

Ideally a woman should not go to an analyst specifically for vaginismus, but rather will seek help to explore her whole personality.

> If a woman asks for a specific cure, an analyst cannot be tied in this way. Having said this, of course it's true that analysts see people who come to them for all kinds of difficulties, and as part of the analysis the difficulty will clear up
> (Lorna Guthrie, Jungian Analyst)

Although I show psychoanalysis in stages, it will tend not to be carried out in this rigid and precise manner. I also use technical terms to describe the process, but I do so simply to familiarize you with the theories upon which this method is based. Let me reassure you that the majority of analysts speak in everyday language and refrain from using jargon. Neither do they force a particular theory onto a woman, nor attempt to make one fit her psychology. When we consult an analyst he will start where he can, and see how it takes shape.

> No well-trained analyst tackles problems head-on in the way that, say, a clinic might. It's a very different approach because there's so much time it allows for things to emerge in their own way
> (Lorna Guthrie, Jungian Analyst)

Naturally, any woman's analysis is considerably more complicated and its journey much more indirect than any simple outline I can possibly show in a few pages. Since every analyst operates within the broadest boundary of possibilities, there can be no typical analysis. Every woman and every analyst is different.

LINDA'S TREATMENT

Working with an Analytical Psychotherapist, this is the method we finally employed to help resolve my vaginismus.

When friends discover I'm being analysed they tend to ask

the same questions: 'But what really happens? How does it work? Do you lie down on a couch?' Analysis seems to be shrouded in secrecy, so I hope this account will demystify what is essentially a healing process. It may be thought of as 'repair work', helping to restart the processes leading to maturity which have been halted.

The need for deeper exploration

Like most people, I knew very little about my unconscious mental processes before I entered analysis. The only person I could think of who'd been in psychoanalysis was Woody Allen . . . this was as far as my knowledge stretched about the subject. I didn't even realise it could help resolve vaginismus.

Although I knew I was suffering from vaginal spasm and desperately wanted help, I didn't know who to approach so I first went to the obvious people – the gynaecologists – as I have already described. I naturally thought the only way to treat what I thought of as a physical problem would be a physical treatment. It didn't work. Unable to tolerate the internal examinations I was left feeling overwhelmed and defeated by the enormity of my condition. I entered analysis 'through the back door', meaning it wasn't a conscious decision on my part. In 1981 at the age of 30 and after almost three years of marriage I made an appointment to see another doctor (my fourth) at a Well Woman Clinic. It so happened that this doctor was an Analytical Psychotherapist, still practising psychosexual medicine part-time. I explained how I'd always felt too small to be penetrated and had an acute phobia about anything entering me. Whenever my lover attempted to penetrate, my vaginal muscles clamped tightly shut and I also felt faint, nauseous, and sometimes even retched. I described my vagina as a 'gaping open wound with bits dangling from inside'. The doctor was able to rule out any physical causes from past medical history (the internal examination described in the last chapter had disclosed there was nothing physically wrong). His original planned treatment was to counsel me, eventually leading up to an internal examination. This psychosomatic approach (as in Tina's

Treatment) seemed less frightening than previous encounters with gynaecologists who had always insisted on examining me first. I was assured that he wouldn't force an examination, that it was to be at my instigation and only when I felt ready. However, this wasn't to be the course of events.

My fears about the internal did not decrease over the subsequent weeks, and into the seventh week of therapy I found myself daydreaming about the doctor. It was approaching Christmas and because of the holidays was not due to see him for another fortnight. During the break I felt anguished; I missed him and longed to see him. I didn't think I could endure another week so I telephoned the clinic. On the telephone he suggested I see him in his capacity as an analyst since a more in-depth therapy now seemed appropriate. I was able to make the transition quite easily from the psychosexual to psychoanalytic setting since I was still seeing the same person.

Officially, once I'd made the request to see him during my holidays, and had also disclosed the romantic nature of the fantasies I was having about him, my psychosexual treatment had ended. Psychoanalysis had begun.

Repairing damaged growth

It is impossible to describe exactly what takes place in more than six years' analysis. There were no dramatic insights or theatrical interpretations leading to the instant relief of spasm. Since the roots of my vaginismus lay in my early development, my experiences and relationships during infancy were to be key sources of information for my analyst. Growth and change are a series of incremental achievements, each slowly building on the other to allow the unlocking of what it is the spasm seeks to block and defend. Most of the insights were painful and difficult to reach since the vaginismus was protecting a multitude of layers, all giving clues to earliest experience, anxiety and assumptions, as well as my needs and fears. The relationship between a woman and her analyst is always a central theme, because the re-enactment of such a close, dependent bond tends to mirror the earlier parental one, helping bring about an understanding and reappraisal of old, and often distorted, assumptions and resolutions we made as a child. Knowing the minimum about my analyst forced me to draw conclusions about things I could not know, thereby giving us the opportunity to recreate left-over feelings and interactions from infancy in the hope this could lead to a better outcome the second time around.

Growth and change are deemed to be taking place when dynamics such as will be described are recognised, identified, understood, separated from the past and, finally, worked through. These are the main routes which can lead to the resolution of conflicts and, ultimately, the reversal of vaginismus.

Free-flowing thought without censorship

We began by asking ourselves 'What are the conflicts which led to Linda's vaginismus?'. My analyst's training taught him that the answer to this question probably lay in the mischannelling of unconscious psychosexual conflicts and an unsatisfactory resolution of the Oedipal Complex. In order to understand how and why this had occurred, he would need to reach the causes lying buried deep in my subconscious. But how did he attempt to reach that part of my mind whose contents remain almost totally inaccessible? He used two techniques:

1.

Free Association: whereby I said whatever came to mind throughout a session. This might not seem bold today, but it was an outrageous and novel idea in Freud's time to encourage patients to speak without repressing any material whatsoever. The kind of information important to my analyst wasn't likely to be gathered by a series of questions as in the normal doctor-patient dialogue. Though answers to specific questions would have provided factual information, this might have been at the expense of wealth of emotional connections which could only be made if I talked freely and uninhibitedly.[6] Aside from initial history-taking, my analyst asked only the minimum and commented occasionally on what I said.

2.

Meanings of Dreams: my analyst saw these as symbolic representations of my unconscious conflicts and repressed erotic wishes.

The other central principles which formed the basis of my analysis were:

Exploration of infantile sexuality

Freud believed as children we come into the world with our sexual instincts and that at each different stage of infantile sexuality, pleasure is obtained from different sexually stimulating ('erotogenic') zones. His general theory was that our libido (sexual drive) in infancy passes through three emotional stages:

(1)   *ORAL (0–18 mths)*

When the baby experiences pleasure from nursing at the breast.

(2)   *ANAL (18 mths–3 yrs)*

When the infant experiences pleasure from her bowel movements.

(3)   *PHALLIC (3–4 yrs)*

When the toddler experiences pleasure from touching her vagina, as in masturbation.

These three stages (and I have only approximated the ages at which they occur) then culminate in the Oedipus phase at ages four or five.[7]

The possibility of us becoming arrested ('stuck') at any of these stages in development might affect our behaviour in later life. A symptom, therefore, expressed in a particular part of our body may indicate (though never precisely) at what stage of development we became 'fixated' (stuck). For example, oral fixation might appear as an anorectic symptom, whilst a phallic fixation might show itself in the vaginismic symptom.* So, the fact that my spasm was located in the area of my vagina gave my analyst clues as to which unconscious forces were active. In other words, my repressed conflicts were of an intimate nature, probably occurring around the phallic (genital) stage.

* Many analysts after Freud, including my own, maintain that the earlier and the less sophisticated the level on which the disturbance is experienced, the more likely it is that the symptoms will be sexual.

I find a common language that has meaning for this
particular person
(Lorna Guthrie, Jungian Analyst)

We needed, then, to find a way of translating the language
of my vagina into the language of my innermost feelings.

My analyst's aim was to unravel and explore with me the
conflict material which my vaginismus was expressing. In
particular, the 'blockage' caused perhaps by my unresolved Oedipus Complex.* The origins of my vaginismus
began in infancy when I felt persecuted by my phantasies,
combined with the discovery I made during this period of
growth. I saw that adults were able to sexually give each
other things that I couldn't, at a time when I was really too
small. As explained in Chapter Three my fear in adulthood
of being 'too small' to accommodate an erect penis was
perhaps another way of saying that my needs, desires and
unnurtured part of myself made me feel I was too small, too
young and too vulnerable.

Aspects of childhood re-enacted with analyst

A couch was used so that my analyst and I didn't distract
one another, encouraging me to focus on myself rather
than on him. Emphasis was on underlying conflicts and
less on the here and now. Sessions lasted 50 minutes (so he
could have a ten-minute break in between patients).
Insistence on the analytic hour and regularity of sessions
also gave me a sense of security and consistency, themes
which felt internally absent.

Treatment was intensive, frequent and lengthy (three
times a week since 1981 and still continuing). This allowed
me to 'regress' (my return to infantile and primitive states)
whereby I repeated and re-enacted earlier unresolved
relationships with my analyst. This sometimes took the
form of experiencing him as the 'Bad Mother' who was
tantalizing, powerful and withholding, or alternatively the
'Good Mother' who nurtured, loved, held and fed me

* Many analysts after Freud regard the period when baby is totally
dependent, not the Oedipal phase, as the stage when psychological
problems may occur in development.

psychologically. Our aim was for a more successful outcome of unresolved primary issues, but this time with him and in a current setting. It was felt that if I was able to enjoy a satisfying, intimate relationship with my analyst, then the persecutory internalized images I carried around inside could be expected to lose their emotional charge.

Interpretation leading to insights

When my analyst made conscious what was emerging in my unconscious this was called an 'interpretation'. An 'insight' is my capacity to understand my own, or someone else's, mental processes, as well as my sudden understanding of a complex situation or problem. However, in real life, realisations and insights may come suddenly in one session, disappear in another, only to return several months later. This made my progress seem patchy, slow and frustrating, unlike the orderly fashion I present in this outline.

One of my analyst's principal tasks was to point out connections between the current vaginismus and events which may have led to it. This included helping me to identify and 'map out' the nature of my emotional processes, for example, why I felt and fantasised the way I did, and the subsequent assumptions I made. As analysis progressed I became increasingly able to make interpretations and connections myself, needing minimum assistance from my analyst.

> The more a woman knows about herself and about being able to link some things from the past and therefore able to be free of some of those things, then the more she is able to make wiser choices in her life (Lorna Guthrie, Jungian Analyst)

Other interpretations included our discovery that muscle spasm was not at the level of my vagina but rather in the areas of love, intimacy, dependency and trust. This was significant since it meant the vaginismus would not need to exist bodily if I could locate the areas in which it truly existed.

Helping me to understand myself more, my analyst drew

to my attention that when I talked about 'the spasm' or 'the vaginismus', this was a natural attempt to distance and separate myself from owning my difficulty. In other words, I wished to avoid the pain and anguish of seeing spasm as the angry, hurt and outraged parts of myself.

Repression

Most psychological traumas of childhood are 'repressed' in order to protect ourselves from pain, and this is when something is pushed into our unconscious, or is kept from becoming conscious. Thoughts and impulses are also repressed if we feel they conflict with conventional ways of behaving and thinking.

Resistance

Internal conflicts about inner changes, happiness and success were reflected in the relationship between me and my analyst. This is called 'resistance' and it usually took the form of my not complying with analytic rules (refusing to use the couch, or asking my analyst personal questions about himself and his life).

Resistance was also a defence against my taking-in of his undesirable and painful interpretations which I experienced as a kind of analytic 'penetration'. However, he never accused me of using resistance or defences as intentional ways of blocking him or my treatment. Rather, the appearance of a defence was seen by him as an opportunity to work through remaining areas of difficulties and conflict.

The past coming alive in the present

Feelings of curiosity, envy and exclusion with regard to my analyst's sex life and lover emerged during analysis. I was recreating an earlier scenario which came alive as the result of my regressing. Therapy revealed that as a baby it was possible I had accidentally witnessed or imagined my parents' lovemaking. The reliving in the present of this early experience allowed me to get in touch with and explore buried emotions and assumptions which resulted from my feelings around the 'primal scene'. I discovered that as a baby I had felt envious and excluded, ashamed and guilty, just as I now felt towards my analyst and my friends. Such negative feelings had led to the assumption that I was wicked, too small and neither woman nor desirable enough ever to be lovingly penetrated. I saw how the themes were strikingly familiar: the exclusion I felt then as a baby and how I felt later as an adult when confronted with (or imagining) other peoples' lovemaking. Before this discovery I often got the sequence of events in the wrong order. I would insist that the vaginismus existed *before* my feelings of outrage towards sexual women. In actual fact, it was the erroneous assumptions I made about myself which had arisen from the exclusion, rivalry, guilt and envy which had led to the vaginismus, not the other way round. Rearranging the sequence of events led to recognition and relief that I wasn't born with vaginal spasm but had developed it as the result of intense emotions which I was emotionally too immature to cope with.

Loving and hating the analyst

Much emphasis was placed on the relationship between me and my analyst in particular my feelings towards him (called 'transference'). Used loosely, transference refers to the interflow between any two people in everyday life.

This consists of our unspoken attitudes, images, ideas, perceptions and mutual feelings of love and hate. But when we use the term 'transference' analytically it refers not only to conscious and unconscious feelings and reactions towards my analyst, but also to those moments when I unconsciously react towards him as if he is an important figure from my psychological past (mother, father). Through the analysing of this transference I wrestled with my past coming alive in the present, and so enabled us to trace these emotions to early infantile anxieties. I wasn't simply remembering painful, repressed experiences but was recreating, repeating and reliving them too. Resolution of transference is seen to be critical to a successful outcome because it mirrors my unresolved Oedipal situation.

Sadly, there are many jokes made about patients falling in love with the analyst, making it seem a laughable and even trivial occurrence. The intensity of feelings a woman might have for the analyst may be more easily understood if we see what he represents in her life. My analyst assumed great importance because he always believed in my worth, autonomy and specialness, as well as my right to his undivided attention and to be taken seriously. The analytic encounter was the first time that many of these needs had been acknowledged or met. Feelings are never acted upon between woman and analyst, but rather they are explored. It is precisely this degree of exploration which distinguishes the analytic relationship from any other that a woman will have in her life.

Loving and hating the patient

So now we turn to the analyst, for he, too, experiences emotions.

The term 'counter-transference' refers to my analyst's feelings and reactions towards me.

> It isn't only the woman who is being explored . . . the analyst is also constantly exploring his own psyche (Lorna Guthrie, Jungian Analyst)

Because he had been analysed (a prerequisite of any analytic training) my analyst was less apt to develop counter-transference. When it did occur he was more able to understand it, thereby avoiding complicating my own problems. If his counter-transference hadn't been understood by him and analysed, it could have distorted his perceptions of me and caused him to act in a manner which may not have been in my best interests. In the course of his own analysis he became aware of his own conflicts and blind spots, and this helped him to avoid reacting automatically to feelings I stirred up in him. If he had acted upon his feelings rather than interpreted or reflected upon them, it might have led him to play out a role which reduplicated an earlier situation in my life.[8] This kind of scenario played out between analyst and patient, and determined by the patient's conflicts, is known as a 'psychodrama'.

Interpretation of conflicts as opposed to reassurance and rational explanations

In contrast with the more directive treatments, my analyst explored why I put up defences of 'not knowing' where my vaginal opening was in order to interpret my conflicts, rather than try to re-educate and reassure me with gynaecological diagrams or self-examination. Rather than appeal to my rationality by re-educating me when I professed ignorance about the size of my vagina, he interpreted my reasons behind this 'ignorance'. In the same way, if a doctor had re-educated me about my anatomy (as both Amy and Ellen were) and I had then subsequently forgotten what I'd been taught, my 'forgetting' would have been analysed as a dramatic demonstration of repressive forces at work.[9]

My inability to allow penetration was also not taken literally in the sense of attempting to stretch my vagina, but rather was seen by him as symbolic of my inability to accept and receive penetrative (loving) interpretations. My analyst refrained from behaving in a direct, friendly or angry manner. His professional detachment, as opposed to constant reassurance, advice and sympathy, was maintained in my interests and not because he didn't feel warmth or empathy towards me. The unique experience he offers me by preserving a neutral attitude is to have him understand how I am feeling, accept it, and help me to understand and work through it myself.[10]

Wider objectives as the goal

Success was never measured simply in my ability to allow penile penetration or the disappearance of spasm. Instead, progress was monitored and acknowledged in more profound ways, some of which include the following:
My ability to

- see where the vaginismus is really located.

- identify the origins and roots of envy and hatred of the sexual and fertile world.

- distinguish my analyst from key (parental) figures.

- notice the past coming alive in the present and how my inner world appears in my outer world.

- own and acknowledge the power of my destructive forces without attacking or blaming myself for needing such defences.

- symbolize during sessions rather than discuss issues at face value.

- understand the connections between penile and analytic intercourse and recognise that the same protective mechanism is in force as a defence against unresolved incestuous feelings being stirred up.

- distinguish between subjective experience and reality: the difference between anxiety and fact.

- notice how I take feelings from the past and make them real and concrete for today.

- distinguish a 'projection' (disowning unacceptable feelings and attributing them to him) from reality.

- experience myself as loving and lovable.

Improvement of the vaginismus which occurred during the course of analysis was regarded as the product of the resolution of my more basic personality problems. We never referred to the vaginismus as a 'sexual problem'. My analyst saw spasm only as a symptom, about which deeper conflicts were involved, so it required a deeper insight. Treatment has not necessarily been terminated because the vaginismus has been resolved, but will rather be concluded when my analyst and I feel the deeper childhood conflicts and transference have been understood and worked through.

Jungian Analysis

Less commonly referred to as 'Analytical Psychology',

Jungian analysis is an in-depth psychotherapy based upon very similar concepts to a traditional analysis. This method was instituted by a Swiss doctor, Carl Gustav Jung, an early associate of Freud from whom he parted in 1913. Whilst the Freudian may ask 'How did Linda develop vaginismus?', the Jungian may ask 'What does Linda's vaginismus symbolize?'

A Freudian will probably see vaginismus as *being* the problem, whereas to the Jungian vaginismus may be seen as a constructive attempt or creative solution to resolve the conflicts which led to vaginal spasm.

Carl Jung did not believe that a woman was driven by sexual instincts, as Freud did, but rather by the myths and symbols of the culture into which she was born. Jung called this the 'collective unconscious'. To the Jungian a dream would be seen as symbols, not solely expressing neurotic symptoms or repressed erotic wishes. So too, vaginismus might be seen as the symbol of closed doors, with the doors being closed from both sides.

Other main differences of a Jungian analysis are that sessions may be less frequent, and a couch is not always used.

WHO BENEFITS MOST FROM PSYCHOANALYSIS?

Those of us who, like me, see vaginismus as part of deeper emotional conflicts and not merely spasm of the vagina may be more suited to a psychoanalytic approach.

Much is spoken of the need for articulacy, intelligence and the ability to express one's feelings if analysis is to be successful. Actually, this isn't 100% true. Language may often be used as a huge intellectual defence, so intelligence and high academic achievements do not automatically guarantee success. It could be argued, for example, that a less educated, less academic woman might not put up such linguistic resistance.

However, there are certain things to be considered. Analysis tends to be a lengthy process, so it is advisable to consider both the financial and emotional commitment before entering into this kind of treatment. As with any therapy, the desire for change is required. Other important factors are a high degree of motivation, a certain amount of objectivity to step back and observe oneself, the ability to symbolize, and a willingness to confront painful issues. A woman needs to have a genuine curiosity about herself and, hardest of all, to be able to tolerate the frustrations inherent in analysis, particularly the painful non-gratification of loving feelings. This may sound a daunting undertaking, but analysis asks little more of us than that we be committed to resolving vaginismus through the exploration of our psyche.

If rapid answers and results are demanded of the therapy, then this is probably not a recommended form of treatment. Analysis does not dwell on the symptom, nor does it answer a woman's questions direct. It is far more interested in knowing why the questions are being asked. Asking and wanting specific advice was generally seen by my analyst as a way of avoiding getting in touch with something deeper and more painful.

FEMINIST PSYCHOTHERAPY

Although we will look at this method separately, feminist therapy is not a particular 'school' in the sense that psychoanalysis or humanistic therapies are. Rather, over the years women have involved themselves in many different forms of self-exploration and have created a distinctive therapeutic approach with which to explore feminine psychology. What is specific to feminist therapy, and why I feel its inclusion is valid, is that it is concerned with understanding a woman's internal and external reality together. It recognises how external events may shape and oppress a woman, at the same time as understanding the autonomy and powerfulness of her internal world.[11] The therapy I am about to describe is not exclusively practised by women, nor is it exclusively sought by feminists. For example, my own analyst was able to explore with me fhe social and cultural factors specific to my family which may have influenced my psychosexual development. Since feminist therapy doesn't differ greatly from any mainstream model of psychotherapy, it may be more helpful if the following is read not as a separate method but as an adjunct to any psychodynamic approach. I am therefore only describing those aspects which differ, are underplayed or may even be missed in a classical type of therapy. Jenny's treatment is recreated using the Feminist Object Relations School* since the term 'feminist psychotherapy' does not refer to any one specific orientation.

JENNY'S TREATMENT

Jenny (34) has been with her partner for four years. Every time her lover tries to enter her during lovemaking, Jenny's vagina goes into spasm. She wanted to resolve the vaginismus and was referred to a therapist. She explained to Jenny that she would explore with her the reasons for vaginismus by putting what Jenny saw as her complicated mother-daughter relationship into a context.

Combining psychoanalysis with sociology and culture

Social and psychoanalytic factors are not seen together in the majority of psychotherapies. One therapist who has developed (and uses) the Feminist-Object-Relations theory told me with irony how she is accused by psychoanalysts of being 'too sociological' and by sociologists of being 'too psychoanalytic'.

> For me, these two are absolutely indivisible. A baby comes into the world and is only a set of possibilities. But it enters a social world, and how that world is organised will help her personality to develop. She enters a culture immediately, based upon gender (Susie Orbach, Psychotherapist)

So how was this approach adopted in Jenny's treatment?

Her therapist listened to how Jenny felt and spoke about her relationships with her parents, but in a particular way, ever aware that Jenny's mother's psychopathology needed to be set within a social as well as psychological context. Jenny's hurt and rage with her mother's seeming inability to 'be there' for her was acknowledged and took up a great deal of the therapeutic interaction. In time, Jenny came to

*As devised and practised by psychotherapists Luise Eichenbaum and Susie Orbach.

see her mother's actions as the consequence of the restrictions and demands that were made of her. However, it is important to understand that the work of Feminist-Object-Relations is not about 'absolving' the mother. Whilst of course in one sense it is, in another it cannot be. Jenny's therapist recognised her pain, and that it was real, and allowed Jenny that space within her therapy.

> If I hear a woman's pain about her mother not meeting her needs, the way we begin to talk about it will not be to do with mother's inadequacy solely, but to do with the surrounding circumstances. That's not to deny the pain of the daughter, but to deal with the whole history of generations of mothers and daughters, unconsciously transmitting their agonies. If a mother can't be there for her in a certain way, this is very different from her being wicked or inadequate
> (Susie Orbach, Psychotherapist)

The difficulties in becoming and being a woman

Because Jenny's therapist had explored and worked through her own pain around oppression in patriarchy, she was more able to acknowledge and validate the way Jenny had been restricted because of her gender.

> My starting point is how one psychologically *becomes* a woman, and the difficulties that one encounters along the way.
> (Susie Orbach, Psychotherapist)

Jenny saw that one of the reasons why her mother was unable to handle Jenny's distress as a child had to do with the fact that Jenny's mother wasn't allowed to have her own distress. It was her mother's personal psychological history which made Jenny's distress seem terrorizing, making her mother want to silence it. Because Jenny lived in a culture (British) where psychological distress is not acceptable, this aspect of her development was looked at by the therapist too.

Mother-Daughter relationship as central theme

In Jenny's therapy there was great emphasis on the relationship between her and her therapist. Together they examined the ways in which their relationship expressed Jenny's terrors, fears, anxieties, longings and desires. Jenny saw that aspects of an earlier relationship were being recreated in the therapeutic setting which were to do with the dynamics between her mother and herself. In the therapy itself, the difficulties with intimacy first experienced in a relationship with a woman were re-experienced and the defences against intimacy that Jenny had developed, the attempt to hide her needs and so on, were brought into the open.

> The concentration always on the father feels so wrong for me in relation to most people, be they boys or girls, because *mothers* raise children
> (Susie Orbach, Psychotherapist)

Towards the end of Jenny's therapy, where some resolution, forgiveness and mourning regarding the rage and disappointment surrounding her mother occurred, her mother's own psycho-social position became more visible to Jenny.

Removing the focus from sex

Rather than seeing Jenny's vaginismus in purely sexual terms as the wish to 'castrate' a man or the desire to have a penis ('penis envy'), Jenny's therapist did not draw upon these Freudian theories. Instead, she encouraged Jenny to make contact with her own symbols and meaning for the vaginismus.

> If a woman describes her vagina as a big gaping hole or wound, my association would be immediately to the lack of contact or love, not the Castration Complex or Penis Envy theories. I wouldn't even have thought in sexual terms. If I do think about the penis and vagina, then that would be as an expression of the *attempt to find and express heterosexual love*
> (Susie Orbach, Psychotherapist)

Jenny and her therapist worked on their instincts that the

vaginismus existed more in the areas of intimacy, love and trust rather than in Jenny's sexuality or in her vagina.

> Vaginismus becomes a defence structure against disappointments in early relationships
> (Susie Orbach, Psychotherapist)

The therapeutic relationship became a place for the establishment of a new intimate relationship that sought to embrace Jenny's past difficulties, hold her, allow her to receive and digest love and nurturing from her therapist, so that Jenny had a secure sense of self, a self that could be 'open' to receiving good things in other relationships . . . and ultimately be able to receive a penis.

WHO BENEFITS MOST FROM FEMINIST PSYCHOTHERAPY?

Obviously, a therapy which includes all aspects of a woman's emotional, social and cultural development would be our optimum choice. However, not all therapists may look at the social aspects of a woman's psychology, despite their methods being sensitive and effective. I hope, though, there will always be enough space and individuality in any woman's therapy for her to feel free to discuss and explore all aspects of early relationships, whether the therapist is male or female, feminist or not.

HOMOEOPATHY

I have chosen to include homoeopathy because it demonstrates how holistic medicine works, and because homoeopathic literature includes far more information on and remedies for vaginismus than traditional medicine.

Derived from the Greek word 'homoios' meaning 'like', homoeopathy is the practice of treating like-with-like. That is, treating vaginismus with a substance diluted many times that produces the same symptom as that displayed by the patient. The founder of homoeopathy was an 18th century German physician, Dr Samuel Hahnemann. He became so appalled at the effects of conventional medicine that it inspired him to establish a new comprehensive system of healing.

VIVIEN'S TREATMENT

Vivien (32) has been married for five years and has not been able to consummate the relationship, and this has led to the breakdown of her marriage. Vivien's first attempt at 18 to engage in intercourse felt so traumatic that she developed a phobia about being penetrated. She was referred to a gynaecologist who stretched ('dilated') her vagina under anaesthesia. Unfortunately, this procedure compounded Viven's fantasy that nothing could enter her painlessly unless rendered unconscious. Finally, her sister (who had returned from India where homoeopathy is more widely practised) suggested this as an alternative treatment and Vivien contacted a practitioner through a recognised association.

The three basic principles

- A medicine which produces the symptoms of a disease in someone healthy, will cure that disease in a sufferer. This is what is meant by the term 'like cures like'.

- The more the remedy is diluted and 'succused' (to systematically bang the bottle containing the remedy) the more effective it becomes. This is known as 'potentization'. By extreme dilution, the curative properties are enhanced and all the poisonous or undesirable side effects are lost. Homoeopaths ensure they give the minimum dose required to effect a cure naturally.

- Remedies are prescribed individually by the study of the whole person (hence 'holistic'), according to the patient's basic temperament and responses.

Curing the woman, not vaginismus

The homoeopath treated Vivien first and foremost rather than her spasm, as homoeopathy recognises that the whole body, mind and spirit is affected when we are sick:

> I don't label the woman 'vaginismic' . . . I treat her in
> total, including her emotions. This is what is meant by
> a 'holistic' approach
> (Dr Kenneth Metson, Homoeopath)

In-depth history of past generations

Vivien's case history of health since birth was taken in
detail by the homoeopath, lasting between one and two
hours. He looked at her physical, spiritual, emotional and
sexual history, carefully recording any traumas and noting
her accompanying feelings, anxieties and experiences.

> The history-taking is extensive. I ask about the
> medical history of parents, her emotional makeup,
> any traumas which occurred . . . I ask about her
> appetite and menstrual cycle. I also ask whether there
> are any chronic diseases which run through her
> family. This is not because we can inherit diseases as
> such, but it's possible to inherit characteristics or
> susceptibility to ongoing problems
> (Dr Kenneth Metson, Homoeopath)

Vivien was also asked some pretty strange questions, such
as did she like thunderstorms, what was her birth like, and
did she drink hot or cold drinks? Concentration was
always placed on treating Vivien, not vaginismus. The
homoeopath didn't automatically prescribe a specific
remedy for spasm because he knows that all women vary in
their responses to a symptom according to their temperament. Instead, he tried to determine Vivien's unique
responses and so was able to prescribe on a more
individual basis.

Overcoming the emotional obstructions

Using a remedy, a homoeopath will also seek to trace the
origins of a woman's vaginismus:

> If a woman has repressed an emotion into her
> unconscious, a homoeopathic remedy can very often

bring this emotion back into her consciousness much as is done in psychoanalysis
(Dr Kenneth Metson, Homoeopath)

However, as with any treatment which seeks to uncover repressed emotional pain, there may be times when a woman's unconscious resistance impedes progress:

Sometimes a remedy will go so far but it just can't quite penetrate the block. In this case I might refer her to a hypnotherapist who uses psychoanalysis. Very often he is able to reach the block and then refers her back to me and treatment progresses
(Dr Kenneth Metson, Homoeopath)

Stimulation of the body's healing energies and power

Most conventional treatments take the view that vaginismus is a direct manifestation of an emotional conflict. Homoeopathy, however, sees vaginal spasm as the body's reaction against the emotional conflict *as it attempts to overcome it*, and the prescribed remedy will seek to stimulate our natural healing responses, rather than suppress any isolated symptoms. A remedy made from natural sources (animal, vegetable or mineral) was finally selected and used to assist Vivien to regain health by stimulating her body's natural forces of recovery. In Vivien's case, her treatment lasted two to three years, whereby she was seen generally once a month. At nearly every visit Vivien was given a remedy appropriate for her at that time. Sometimes she noted dramatic changes in her energy and responses, particularly after the first visit, and at other times the changes were very subtle.

We are governed by a vital force which makes us tick, think and feel. If this vital force is unbalanced in any way it is going to produce a symptom, whether it be physical or emotional. Homeopathic medicine aims to correct the imbalance of the vital force allowing our body to respond and correct that imbalance to eventually correct the vaginismus
(Dr Kenneth Metson, Homoeopath)

WHO BENEFITS MOST FROM HOMOEOPATHY?

Homoeopathically, vaginismus is not seen in isolation, but rather freedom from the symptom and realising the full potential of the woman become the ultimate goals. Ideally, all treatments for vaginismus should follow this 'whole person' approach, rather than look at the separate parts of one's body. Homoeopathy also attempts to intervene as little as possible by promoting the body's natural healing powers to come forth. It does not call upon surgery, drugs or other devices:

> If a woman with vaginismus wants to be treated without the use of surgery, drugs or mechanical instruments, then she should consider homoeopathy
> (Dr Kenneth Metson, Homoeopath)

However, as Dr. Metson explains, because holistic medicine is still not as widely known or available as conventional, he tends to treat patients who haven't responded to other traditional methods:

> Women with vaginismus often come to me as the last resort, having tried the conventional treatments. Because I treat her, not spasm, I think that's where homoeopathy scores
> (Dr Kenneth Metson, Homoeopath)

Homoeopathy appeals most to the woman who wants not only to resolve vaginismus but also improve her health on every level. Since it is gentle, natural and unintrusive, homoeopathy may be used in conjunction with any other therapy of her choice. This could be taken as a symbolic expression of our openness, trust and willingness to be supported by several methods in healing vaginismus. Often a new-found interest in regaining our full health may lead us to become interested in other alternative ways of living, including a more nutritious diet, taking up Yoga classes, massage or other gentle forms of body work and relaxation.

SURGERY

I feel ambivalent about even mentioning surgery, since I don't consider it an appropriate treatment for vaginismus.

However, I decided it belonged somewhere in the treatments section simply because: women have unfortunately been operated on for vaginismus in the past, and they still may be misguided into believing surgery is an appropriate way of resolving vaginismus.

I find it difficult to believe that surgery would ever seriously be considered an appropriate method of resolving a psychosomatic condition. Furthermore, when viewed in the climate of today's woman who is asserting control over her own body, surgery for vaginismus seems almost an anachronism.

What does surgery involve?

Suggested treatments for vaginismus in the 1800s were always surgical, and gynaecologists often performed operations on women without consulting a psychiatrist.[12] This is mainly because psychotherapy was still an undeveloped field, and until the advent of Freud the notion of 'talking through' an emotional problem to lead to the resolution of a symptom was unheard of. Basically, there are two physical procedures which doctors carry out to resolve vaginal spasm:

1.

Mechanical therapy:

This is where a woman's vagina is widened and stretched ('dilatated') by a doctor with the help of a speculum or digital (finger) examination.

2.

Surgical treatment:

This involves far more drastic intervention than the first method. An instrument is used to clip off the hymen and a vertical incision is made on each side of the vaginal opening. The stitches cross from side to side and the vulva thus widened. A slender cylindrical instrument (called a 'vaginal bougie') is then inserted into the vagina to dilate it.

Why are physical methods employed?

If we look at mechanical therapy, the reason given for using this method is that the doctor (as an 'authority' figure) is giving the woman permission to have intercourse by physically intervening. However, Prof. Dr H. Musaph, a Dutch specialist, reports that this technique hardly ever produces results. He argues that if this theory of 'permission' is correct then the same result could be achieved simply by talking with the woman and helping her to accept her sexuality and its functions in a more positive way. He further adds that the disadvantage of dilatation is the denial of unconscious, infantile conflicts which led to the vaginismus in the first place. He points out that using this kind of educational/rational approach may actually thwart the explorative psychotherapeutic treatment.[13] A consultant surgeon in obstetrics and gynaecology at a London teaching hospital also confirms that dilatation of the vagina under anaesthetic is never successful in reversing psychological vaginismus.

What is the reasoning behind surgery? The explanation often given is that if the vaginal opening is widened forcefully, vaginismus can no longer occur. Whilst this is correct in that our bodies are no longer able to go into spasm, psychologically they still can. Furthermore, the last link of the psychological process which caused the vaginismus has been tampered with, preventing psychotherapeutic reversal.[14]

One of the reasons why surgery has been suggested or performed is because vaginismus has been mistakenly diagnosed by doctors as an impenetrable hymen. As a result of this clinical confusion, the hymen has been surgically removed but doesn't provide the woman with a cure.[15] Kaplan warns that despite being anatomically successful, the use of surgery gives rise to adverse reactions and problems of sufficient severity to contraindicate its use.[16]

Why surgery is inappropriate for vaginismus

The weight of opinion today is firmly opposed to its use as a treatment for vaginismus. Prof. Dr Musaph has written that over the years he has seen many vaginismic women who underwent surgery yet still had spasms of the thighs or anus, just as before the operation. In others, he observed even more serious after-effects such as inability to orgasm, frigidity and an aversion to intercourse – all problems which are not generally common to women with vaginismus. It wasn't difficult for the doctor to link these symptoms with the surgery the women had undergone. He considered these new problems they were experiencing to be a 'shift' of symptoms, one of the most striking being hypersensitivity of the whole vulva, strongest at the vaginal entrance, making efforts at intercourse seem like torture for the woman. He strongly advises that surgery never be performed for vaginismus, since it hampers and reduces the possibilities for successful psychotherapy.[17]

Such a view is also expressed by Dr Draper, who said that it's more difficult to treat a woman who's had surgery or mechanical dilatation 'because you are just pushing the dilators in against her prevailing fantasies'. She further adds:

> A lot of gynaecologists are still treating vaginismus surgically, but in our studies we found not a single woman needed operating on. A spasm is due to the ideas behind it, it's not a physical thing that you can cut away at. One should try to get to the ideas . . . what it is she is protecting
> (Dr Katharine Draper, Member Inst. Psychosexual Medicine)

As well as surgery causing a shift in the location of spasm rather than its reversal, there are other psychological side effects which should be noted. Any gynaecological procedure performed under anaesthesia may be charged with fantasy-meaning for a vaginismic woman, so it is crucial that the emotional implications are discussed. This is so that any unconscious conflicts may be understood rather than acted upon.[18] I say this because in some instances it will be the woman who requests surgery and not the doctor:

> I think that the times when a patient has been referred to me with a suggestion that surgery might be necessary, the request has usually originally come from the woman herself who has built up the belief that her vagina is indeed physically too small
> (Susan Tuck, Consultant Gynaecologist & Obstetrician)

Virgin Wives points out that in performing surgery to stretch the vagina, a doctor might even be unconsciously colluding with her to consider her vaginismus as purely physical. As we've already seen, many of us share the fantasy that our vagina is too small or deformed, which has no basis in fact. What effect could it have on us and our therapy if the surgeon shows by his actions that he shares our fantasy, and tries to enlarge us by means of an operation?[19]

In Chapter Three I described the stages in psychological development which particularly relate to the onset of vaginismus. What if, during the course of therapy, we get in touch with feelings of unconscious anger or envy towards men ('penis envy/castration complex') or towards our doctor? Could we not then perceive the subsequent surgery as retaliation and punishment by our male therapist for having such fantasies in the first place?[20]

Virgin Wives also reports that the doctor is at risk of acting out a woman's unexpressed fantasy of being raped if he stretches her vagina under anaesthesia. This is confirmed after some women awaken from the operation to exclaim how lovely 'it' had been, and how much they'd enjoyed 'it'. This was understood to be a woman alluding to her unconscious wish that her first intercourse be rape, especially if she has always had an excessive irrational fear of pain. Because of the surgery she has been allowed to act this fantasy out with the doctor in that he painlessly 'rapes' her under gas.[21] Certainly, these aspects of surgery all demonstrate the need to help us understand ourselves better through our fantasies, not to encourage us to act upon them.

The therapists' views

Without exception, all the practitioners I met who treat vaginismus were appalled to learn that surgery was still being suggested or performed. One doctor, in seeking to understand and explain why surgery is performed suggests that perhaps the gynaecologist feels so powerless he has got to do something forceful. Another doctor further explains that because medicine has become successful at doing so many things over the last three decades, many surgeons feel they must do something to make a woman better, and feel very helpless if they can't.

To some, the surgeon's knife for vaginal spasm was a kind of attack on the sufferer:

> I think it's barbaric and is the equivalent of doing female circumcision
> (Dr Paul Brown, Consulting Clinical Psychologist)

> It's horrific . . . the woman must feel she is about to be attacked, but instead of a penis it will be a knife
> (Jill Curtis, Psychotherapist)

Jill Curtis adds that a lot of women's consciousness today is in not having to accept operations like this any more, and seeing there are other ways of being treated:

> Women's bodies are belonging to themselves now, and I'd like to think this book will help them bolt out the door if surgery is suggested for vaginismus

Marianne Granö expresses a similar view with regard to women's ownership of their bodies:

> Because of masturbation and the use of tampons, more and more girls are taking their own hymens, so it's no longer in the hands of the man or the surgeon
> (Marianne Granö, Sexual Psychotherapist, Sweden)

Thankfully, the use of surgery appears to be increasingly abandoned in the United Kingdom, though national statistics still indicate approximately 130 'dilatations under anaesthesia' per year.[22] Unfortunately, the data does not confirm whether surgery was carried out for vaginismus as the diagnosis given is dyspareunia which, as we know, may be a hidden form of vaginismus. I have, however, managed to examine in more detail the statistics of one London Regional Health Authority. Their data clearly indicates that 39 'vaginismus operations' were performed during 1985 and 1986.[23]

Surgery is most inappropriate for vaginismus. Operations performed on the vagina only remain an option for women who are born without a vagina or whose vagina has been narrowed by previous cancer surgery.

DRUGS, TRANQUILLIZERS AND BIOFEEDBACK

My distaste for surgery is followed closely by other invasive methods such as:

Valium (Diazepam)

Used intravenously (injected into a vein) to break through the vicious cycle of fear-spasm-fear-spasm. The choice of tranquillizer is generally determined by the way a woman feels. If vaginismus is secondary then Valium may be appropriate, but if the vaginismus is a repressed anxiety (which needs to be made conscious) then its use would be inappropriate since it would only suppress the anxiety.

Narcotics

A drug such as Methohexitone Sodium is injected in order to:

- trace trauma
- combat strong psychic tension

Barbiturates

Sedatives such as Librium or Valium used as sleeping powders and taken orally before going to bed to decrease anxiety and muscle tension.

Biofeedback

This is where a set of graded electromagnetic (electrical) probes are used as an aid to learning muscle control.

Whilst all the above are suggested as adjuncts to therapy, their invasive nature does not seem synonymous with a natural process aimed at helping us understand ourselves more, and another consideration is the side-effects of such toxic drugs.

WILL OUR PARTNER BE INVOLVED IN THE TREATMENT OF VAGINISMUS?

Now that you've read the individual treatments you will already know which of the methods involves one's partner and which do not. It might be helpful if we can understand the reasons why a partner is or is not brought into therapy. Of course, there are no set rules about this, and two therapists of similar orientation may have differing views on the value of a partner in therapy.

Our partners are already involved, because a lover rarely remains untouched by a woman's vaginismus. As we saw in Chapter Two the presence of spasm in a relationship will always directly affect the partner, even if her therapy appears not to. However, the extent to which the partner is involved in treatment very much depends upon the way vaginismus is interpreted. For example, it is standard practice in Masters and Johnson's approach to treat couples together, since they firmly believe vaginismus is always the product of a couple's disturbed interactions, both contributing to the disorder. Whilst this may be true of some sexual problems, I find it difficult to see how a man can be the cause of his partner's spasm if she had spasm prior to meeting him, or prior to any sexual activity.

The partner in therapy

Some therapists always involve a partner in treatment:

> Right from the word 'Go' he is always present
> (Dr Paul Brown, Consulting Clinical Psychologist)

However, because your partner is required to be involved in treatment this doesn't necessarily imply that he has sexual difficulties quite apart from, rather than related to, the vaginismus. Dr Brown explains his reasons for involving the man:

> There is a difficulty which I've seen in some men that at the point of wanting to introduce an erection in his partner he has become sensitized and rather clumsy due to previous failures. Some work sometimes has to go on with him
> (Dr Paul Brown, Consulting Clinical Psychologist)

Marianne Granö also expresses concern for the partner:

> A partner must have some support. When a man has been waiting for his lover for years and she starts suddenly to want something, often he can be impotent. What they are doing in Holland* is that when they begin group therapy for vaginismic women,/they also start a group for the partners
> (Marianne Granö, Sexual Psychotherapist, Sweden)

Other therapists involve the partner at different stages, not requiring him to be present at every session:

> I prefer to see the couple together initially. I can observe what their relationship is like and allow them to talk. It's generally quite apparent then which is the more dominant person
> (Barbara Lamb, Nurse Psychosexual Counsellor)

As explained, therapy should never be rigid and should allow for individual requirements. This flexibility is demonstrated when speaking about the partner:

> Sometimes I involve the partner, but not always. We have a kind of round-table discussion where we work out what the woman wants
> (Dr Martin Cole, Sex Therapist)

This view is also shared by a psychotherapist:

> I don't insist on involving him, though I would ask why she comes alone. If she says that her lover isn't interested, *then* I get interested and ask him to come for one or two sessions
> (Marianne Granö, Sexual Psychotherapist, Sweden)

And a doctor:

> Although sometimes the partner is involved, I wouldn't think of it initially. I would listen to what the woman says about him without needing to see him myself. If he

* See page 181 for 'Vaginismic Women's Group With Parallel Partners Group'.

> seems to have a problem in his own right, then I would
> find him help somewhere
> (Dr Robina Thexton, Member Inst. Psychosexual Medi-
> cine)

If it is Couples Group Therapy then it goes without saying the woman will attend with her partner. As we will see in a Vaginismus Group, the partner may be brought in later if there seems to be additional problems impeding progress.

Therapies which don't involve the partner

However, there are some treatments which do not involve the partner, because they work strictly on an individual basis. These would be in the psychotherapeutic and psychoanalytic settings. If other people are brought in then the transference between analyst and patient may be altered and diluted, and the repressed infantile conflicts may not emerge so distinctly.

> I wouldn't involve a woman's partner because that
> isn't the way I work. I might well suggest that he
> might like to see someone else, because sometimes
> the partner gets left behind
> (Jill Curtis, Psychotherapist)

Unlike directive behavioural approaches, psychodynamic therapy is confined on a one-to-one basis so that the focus is on the woman presenting with vaginismus. In some instances she may not even have a partner, but if she does, then any information gained (or not gained) about him and the quality of their relationship will emanate from the woman, and the partner will not be allowed to attend sessions with her. Vaginismus is seen as part of a woman's emotional conflicts, the origins of which have nothing to do with the current sexual partner in her life.

Of course, she may have unconscious reasons for choosing to be with him, and she may transfer her unresolved conflicts onto this partner or previous partners, but a psychoanalyst would not see the partner as the key figure in her life . . . he will be concentrating on much earlier figures from her past.

The psychodynamic approach seeks to help a woman

understand her unconscious choice of partners. Once she has understood her responses and recognises they are in answer to unresolved conflicts, and she is then able to work through any remaining difficulties, the need to remain in an unhappy relationship or exhibit the spasm will no longer be strong. The analyst will be concerned rather to ease the vaginismus until its hold and strength dissolves through its not being needed any more. Resolution will include the investigation and working through the painful conflicts that the woman has had to repress, but this would be the attempt to end the psychological conditions that made her ripe for vaginismus to develop and continue, not alter or support the partner.

PART II
WORKING IN GROUPS

Vaginismus may also be treated within a controlled group setting where there is generally more than one therapist working with the group.

COUPLES-GROUP ANALYTIC THERAPY

Deriving from psychoanalysis, group therapy was originally designed to make therapy more widely available, and allows for emotional problems to be played out and worked through in a small group rather than individually. One method is 'Group Therapy' where eight or so people (formerly strangers) are brought together. The other method aimed at treating marital and sexual problems (including vaginsimus) is known as 'Couples-Group Therapy'.

DIANE & TIM'S TREATMENT

Diane (28) has lived with Tim (29) for the past two years. She has never been able to insert tampons and believed her vagina must be abnormally small or deformed. Consequently, she had always anticipated pain during intercourse and had never been able to tolerate penetration. She began to see a sex therapist but stopped treatment about a year ago as she didn't feel it was helping her. She felt isolated and wanted to share her vaginismus with other people, and both she and Tim decided on a couples group.

A collection of people to mirror everyday relationships

Diane and Tim's group was considered therapeutically valuable because, like other well-selected therapy groups, it mirrored family and society. Any unconscious conflicts in the members will shape their behaviour in the group, and with the therapist's help everyone began to understand these connections. Diane and Tim were encouraged to express their thoughts and feelings so that their fellow members could respond to what they were sharing. Everyone was encouraged to discuss, interpret, empathise and sometimes perhaps challenge what was being said. Diane and Tim learned to do the same for the other members in turn. The aim was for the couples to see themselves and their problems more objectively through feedback from others, and therefore reconcile themselves to what they really were so that they became less anxious. The group leader (therapist) who conducted the group did so in the same style he would conduct individual therapy and so depending upon his orientation and personality he could be expected to be detached, involved or challenging.

Supporting and being supported by others

One of the benefits of Diane and Tim's group was the opportunity for them to communicate and share their feelings in safety with more than one person. Diane and Tim were told that although there might not be another woman in the group experiencing the same degree of vaginismus, some other female members would almost always understand since everyone had usually experienced something similar, if less troubling. Though there was only occasionally a focus on Diane's vaginismus, a good deal of time was devoted to sharing about sexual difficulties in general.

I don't usually explore the details of the sexual symptomology in great detail, because it makes little difference to what I do, or to the result. However, people do report out of the blue that their difficulty has disappeared. The fact that they mention the problem in the group seems to lead to a resolution of the problem without any actual discussion of it
(Dr Robin Skynner, Group Analyst)

Couples-Group Therapy for a specific type of vaginismus

In the couples groups we've had many couples with extreme degrees of sexual difficulty, which I'm pretty sure included vaginismus. They've complained of inability to bear penetration, so I've little doubt that the muscular spasm was there
(Dr Robin Skynner, Group Analyst)

Some sexual difficulties reportedly do very well in a group such as the one Diane and Tim were members of. As long as there are accompanying personality problems or sexual inhibitions relating to the vaginismus, this type of group is appropriate. However, if the vaginal spasm is more specific, localized or due to a trauma then these women may find the more direct methods (i.e. behavioural and sex therapies) more appropriate.

I have never tried it, but my experience suggests that an extremely powerful form of therapy for vaginismus with the more straightforward cases would be in a group* of women who all suffer from that symptom, led by someone with a good understanding of it
(Dr Robin Skynner, Group Analyst)

Less individual attention

This type of therapy is less expensive than individual therapy, and it may also be available in the National Health Service. Members do not receive as much individual attention from a therapist, as they would be in a one-to-one

(* See *Jo's Treatment* page 170)

setting (such as in Maureen's, Jenny's or Linda's treatments) but there are other advantages which compensate because when a group works well there are eight sources of support and understanding, rather than one. It could be that some of us might need different types of therapies at differing stages of our lives. In this way it's quite possible for a woman to begin with group work and then, like Diane, gain further insight and the wish to expand by going into individual therapy later.

WHO BENEFITS MOST FROM COUPLES-GROUP THERAPY?

Like Diane, if a woman doesn't feel individual therapy is for her then a couples-group might be the starting place for exploration of hidden conflicts. It should be recognised that a couples-group may only be appropriate and effective for the woman whose vaginismus is part of a deeper personality problem as opposed to a more 'straightforward' case.

If a woman is particularly anxious and vulnerable about disclosing herself to others, she might do better with the closer more nurturing relationship that an individual therapist offers.

I feel that since the origins of vaginismus lie in the area of early intimacy and sexuality, individual therapy seems more appropriate for exploring the difficulties we have around an intimate act such as intercourse. Vaginismus prevents the ultimate in closeness and trust: the act of penetration. Isn't it possible that the wish to avoid such intimacy, dependency, trust and closeness, all inherent in individual therapy, might be an unconscious reason for a woman with vaginismus choosing group therapy?

However, one Group Analyst explains it is unlikely that any woman with vaginimus would choose group therapy as a first option. Usually it is sought after the failure of other individual treatments:

> In an intimate matter of this kind one would always think of individual sessions, or at least sessions just with the one couple, and that is how I usually begin. But it is fair to say that many cases of severe sexual inhibition,

probably including vaginismus, have responded well to couple-groups after the failure of a long series of analytic and behavioural individual methods
(Dr Robin Skynner, Group Analyst)

VAGINISMUS GROUP THERAPY

As the result of research carried out in 1980 in the National Health Service, it was decided that because groups had been successful in treating women's other sexual problems, vaginismus might also be treated within a group situation.[24] Groups tend to be small (four women in each) and the method used is behavioural therapy. In general, two therapists would run a vaginismus group, and the diagnosis would be made by them before the start of treatment. Groups consist of seven weekly sessions lasting one hour.

JO'S TREATMENT

Jo (25) has been living with her boyfriend for three years. Because she could not insert tampons she believed her vagina was abnormally constructed and consequently feared penetration. During the last two years she had tried two different treatments, but neither had helped her. These failures increased Jo's sense of isolation and inadequacy. After hearing about group therapy on a radio programme, she asked her GP if he could refer her for this type of treatment as she felt the need of contact and support.

Success in a group when other methods have failed

Usually the women who come are the ones where everything else has failed, so the group is the last thing to be tried
(Dr Patricia Gillan, Consultant Psychologist)

Like Jo, many of the women who arrive at group therapy do so because they have not been able to work in any other setting. The co-therapists heard some of the reasons why the women had rejected the other methods.

Some said how unpleasant and rushed the examinations were. They spoke of the glass dilators and their
fears that they would break inside them. All of this
had made them more tense
(Dr Patricia Gillan, Consultant Psychologist)

The womens' relationships with each other

At times, Jo's group was competitive and self-critical
because it wasn't just the therapists giving their views; the
other women in the group were also encouraged to express
how they felt about one another. Because most women
with vaginismus feel the need to hide their problem, Jo
found it very reassuring to meet other women with the
same condition. All the women were after the same target,
and so the competition within the group was seen to be
healthy.

All sorts of things are operating in groups. Say if one
woman improves a bit, then another woman wants to
join in her pleasure and be at the same rate
(Dr Patricia Gillan, Consultant Psychologist)

Helping the group to help themselves

Sessions took place in a large room of a teaching hospital.
Jo, the other women and the co-therapists all sat on chairs
in a circle. The aims were to help Jo and the group to try and
work out a method of self-help.

The aims of a vaginismus group are to try and change
attitudes toward the problem, to share experiences so
that the women don't feel isolated. It's a very caring
atmosphere
(Dr Patricia Gillan, Consultant Psychologist)

The *first session* consisted of Jo introducing herself to the
other group members. They then shared with each other
how they felt about their vaginismus.

Much of this session was spent explaining the general
outline of therapy, physical examinations and homework
tasks.

Jo and the group were taught how to relax, how to touch their vaginas and find the clitoris. No touching or self-examination ever took place in the sessions; these exercises were given to do as 'homework' at home.

> We ask them to imagine they are about half an inch high, and are climbing up their thigh . . . what would they find inside their vagina? From their descriptions we get an idea how each woman feels about herself
> (Dr Patricia Gillan, Consultant Psychologist)

Ongoing discussions of progress and difficulties

Session Two involved a discussion of homework for Jo and the group; this was a regular procedure throughout all the sessions.

> Each woman would know what progress each of the others was making. This is nice because it's a sharing of details
> (Dr Patricia Gillan, Consultant Psychologist)

During this session the structure and function of the vagina and the PC muscles were discussed and illustrated by slides. PC muscle exercises were given throughout the therapy (as they were to Amy and Ellen) to help Jo gain awareness of vaginal control.

> We ask the women to try and introduce one finger into their vaginas, and then to increase this to two. We also encourage them to insert tampons
> (Dr Patricia Gillan, Consultant Psychologist)

Sessions Three to Five consisted of talking about thoughts and feelings associated with.their homework exercises. Group discussion dealt with Jo's emotional and intellectual responses to self-stimulation and various suggestions regarding rhythm and variety of touch were offered. Jo's group also engaged in role playing orgasm in an exaggerated manner to encourage them to abandon themselves. The exaggeration took the form of increased vocal sounds, movement and grimaces.

In the *Sixth session* discussion centred on sharing all

previous experiences and activities with Jo's partner. It was suggested this should begin in a non-threatening manner such as non-genital focusing, progressing to finger penetration, then genital sensate focusing and eventually intercourse (as in Amy's treatment). Once Jo was able to achieve two finger insertion she was encouraged to introduce her lover's fingers into her vagina.

> Every woman has her own time factor, and some
> women take longer to achieve each stage
> (Dr Patricia Gillan, Consultant Psychologist)

Jo was encouraged to use fantasies when touching her body, and at this stage the group discussed the homework tasks they were now undertaking with their partners.

The *Seventh and final session* was a review meeting in which Jo was given the opportunity to discuss at length any doubts or difficulties she was experiencing. If any of the women had been unable to achieve the tasks then they might have been offered individual or couple sessions once the group had ended.

WHO BENEFITS MOST FROM A VAGINISMUS GROUP?

Reflecting the diversity in personalities and preferences, some of us do not do well with the probing exploratory therapies. Equally, others do poorly with a behavioural programme that is so rigid it uses dilators and nothing much else. If, like Jo, we feel we have exhausted all the other methods then we might find the additional support and encouragement of a group setting more appropriate.

Of course, we may select group therapy as our first choice, and not because we have been unsuccessful with other methods.

As with any group situation, therapists are unable generally to work to a pace that suits each individual. However, this need not be a disadvantage because if a single member can't progress onto the next stage this would be talked through as part of the group therapy process to offer support, guidance and encouragement. Another benefit of the group setting is that it can act as a good motivator. When one woman succeeded in finger penetration this inspired Jo and the others, who then wanted to achieve this after having proof of success. Jo particularly found the group a stimulant to carrying out her homework tasks as opposed to individual therapy where the element of inter-support felt missing. This meant Jo had often attended individual sessions without having carried out her tasks.

Regrettably, because of financial cut-backs in the health service, Vaginismus Groups may not be so widely available as other treatments.

SEXUALITY GROUP

This is a structured group of 6 to 8 women consisting of two-hourly sessions and lasting from 8 to 10 weeks. The women who lead the groups are trained to work from a place of their own vulnerability. In other words, the leader isn't seen as the 'expert' but rather as one who can identify and feel anguish with a woman's fear of being abnormal. The aim of a sexuality group is to provide a safe and supportive atmosphere in which women may share their feelings. Many women feel unsafe talking about their sexuality, and because of the competition between us it's often difficult for us to be supportive. The approach of a sexuality group is affirmative and positive to try and counteract both the negativity and competition about women's sexuality in our culture.

AMANDA'S GROUP

Amanda is 26 and lives with her parents. She always had an excessive fear about her vagina, particularly that it felt too small to allow penetration. Amanda had never been able to share her vaginismus with anybody, and a series of different treatments had not helped her resolve her spasm. She heard about the sexuality group through a girlfriend.

The programme

The elements of sensitivity, trust and sharing were incorporated into a programme which focused on women's sexuality. The accent was on education to help counteract lack of information and permission a woman receives to enjoy her own sexuality. Because Amanda had never been able to share her vaginismus before it was tremendously healing to be able to share it safely in such a group.

> The group setting is very important because the actual process of seeing different anxieties and problems gives a woman a learning experience which is more than in a one-to-one relationship. They realise the cultural implications; that it isn't just the woman with her individual background but it's a much bigger picture
> (Anne Dickson, Sexuality/Assertiveness Trainer & Author)

Some of the themes discussed, shared and explored in Amanda's group throughout the ten weeks were:
Self image & self esteem
– ambivalence in being a woman and the wish to free ourselves from the need for approval

Body image
– negativity towards our vaginas

Self-exploration
– involving looking at, touching and drawing our vagina

Masturbation
– exploring the myths surrounding this activity

Arousal
– understanding what can impede and improve enjoyment

The role of fantasy
– exploring erotic imaginings and the cultural stereotypes

Orgasm
– removing the goal orientation towards this and understanding our physiological responses

Feelings & Emotions
– discovering past events or relationships which we haven't sufficiently grieved over

Sexual likes & dislikes
– identifying what we want and don't want for ourselves

Celebration of our womanhood
– removing the competition and criticism we feel about our, and other women's, bodies

Partners
– exploring our relationships with past and present lovers

The contract

Amanda and the group were asked to plan what they specifically wanted from the course. This was called a 'contract'.

> I feel very strongly that women shouldn't be told what to do. I help them work out what they want for themselves by making a list and we then work out the stages to get there
> (Anne Dickson, Sexuality/Assertiveness Trainer & Author)

Expressing what Amanda really wanted from the group was seen as an important step in her taking charge and feeling comfortable with her own sexual responses and needs. Feeling less guilty about such needs changed the way Amanda looked at other people in terms of getting others to meet those needs.

Going back to the beginning

Amanda shared her vaginismus and the pain and secrecy surrounding it with the other women. Although the others had come to the group for different reasons, there was much empathy and sensitivity expressed towards Amanda and her vaginismus.

> There's a lot of room in a group to allow a woman to be different and yet also to belong
> (Anne Dickson, Sexuality/Assertiveness Trainer & Author)

Amanda's past history and experiences were also shared and looked at within the group.

One of the most moving things I've ever experienced was one vaginismic woman's presentation of her 'story'. She described to us the last five years of her having vaginismus and the treatments she's been through
(Anne Dickson, Sexuality/Assertiveness Trainer &Author)

The other women also shared their personal 'stories' and the reasons why they had come to the group. One of the first things Amanda did in the exploration of her sexuality was to try and understand how she had learned to behave the way she did.

We start off right at the beginning, taking a behavioural approach to the problem. This is a process of talking and looking at the messages we've learned about our bodies and our sexuality
(Anne Dickson, Sexuality/Assertiveness Trainer & Author)

Learning to love our bodies

The group focused on body image, and each woman was encouraged to explore her own vagina with the aid of a mirror. Information was given about women's sexual responses and Amanda learned how the impact of past and present emotions can interfere with sexual activity.

Most women don't understand how anxiety impedes sexual arousal. Because of the pressure to always perform we don't allow ourselves to listen to what's going on with our bodies
(Anne Dickson, Sexuality/Assertiveness Trainer & Author)

Like many of the women in her group, Amanda's vagina remained a negative and very impersonal part of herself. She was encouraged to examine, touch, look at and draw her genitals to help affirm their uniqueness and enable her to become familiar with this part of her anatomy.

Emotions were not seen by the leader as overwhelming or negative, and so when Amanda or the others wept and expressed anger this was experienced as part of the learning process.

> As the result of emotions experienced in the group some women decide they want to explore further and seek individual therapy later. However, although we can touch on these issues, therapy is not within the workshop framework
> (Anne Dickson, Sexuality/Assertiveness Trainer & Author)

Celebration of the inner and outer woman

In one of the sessions Amanda and the group unclothed and had the opportunity to look at each other in a non-critical and non-competitive atmosphere.

> This for me is a real strike for ancient freedoms when women can look at each others' bodies, regaining that childlike ability to look and accept without judging
> (Anne Dickson, Sexuality/Assertiveness Trainer & Author)

The first two-thirds of Amanda's course dealt with her needs and her enjoyment of sex for herself. Towards the latter part of the course Amanda looked at her relationships with men. At this stage the group was encouraged to bring their partners into discussions in preparation for finishing the course.

WHO BENEFITS MOST FROM A SEXUALITY GROUP?

Although a Sexuality Group cannot be called a 'treatment' in the sense that it isn't carried out by a doctor or therapist in a clinical setting, it can nevertheless form part of a valuable process in helping a woman to own her vagina and the accompanying fears and feelings.

> I believe with enough time, support, care, permission and information we can beam a bit of love into that particular muscle to allow a woman with vaginismus to let go

(Anne Dickson, Sexuality/Assertiveness Trainer & Author)

The lack of control women feel they have over their lives, their social powerlessness and the connection of this to their low self-esteem and self-image are reasons why women coming together in a sexuality group can be a very soothing and healing experience. Whilst the self-help element may not necessarily be compatible with the 'expert's' philosophy of treating vaginismus, it nonetheless demonstrates the potential power and creativity we, as women, have in overcoming our vaginismus. A Sexuality Group, therefore, may be more appropriate for the woman who prefers to work outside of the conventional expert-led treatments.

SELF-HELP GROUPS

A self-help group is a beginning, it's not an end. The other women in my group are actively in therapy, but at least they know there are other sufferers
(Jan)

As discussed in Chapter Four, some women are relieved and delighted if they're able to accomplish self-examination of their vagina. However, if this kind of self help is impossible to carry through, a woman should never feel she has to struggle alone in resolving vaginismus.

Whilst supportive, valuable and validating, self-help groups are no substitute for one-to-one or group therapies. Perhaps we shouldn't consider self-help groups as a 'treatment' but rather a means of integrating longed-for outside support into a woman's inner world.

I used to wonder if there was anywhere I could write, though I don't think I'd have had the courage to start my own group. I'd never heard of self help groups but I would have liked to have met with other sufferers
(Sarah)

Feeling defeated by our own failures

Repeated failures at self-help may produce a defeatist

attitude in which vaginismus is seen as insoluble or too huge for anybody to deal with. My own experience confirms that some self help groups may have limited insight and value, simply because each woman is struggling with her own turmoil without any leader/ therapist to intervene and guide her.

Struggling alone against powerful conflicts

Despite the abundance of sex manuals providing instruction and encouragement to enjoy and improve sexual intercourse, there is no firm evidence that they help resolve problems, or that the techniques are efficient. The conflicts which caused our vaginismus are not, regrettably, going to yield easily to self questioning. This is why the techniques for self-discovery can only go so far without another person (the therapist) trained specifically to help in an objective way. This is particularly true of vaginismus, the buried causes of which may be struggled with alone in vain, seeming far more powerful than any conscious willpower at the woman's disposal.

Nevertheless, self-help groups do have a lot to offer some women. The worst that might happen in such a group is that we find our specific needs aren't being taken into consideration enough, and this might then lead us on to seeking individual and more structured help, using the group simply as support. Whilst a self help group cannot be seen as a total therapy in itself, the value of women coming together to share their experiences and give mutual support should never be under estimated. This is especially true for vaginismus, as it is not an easily shared or understood problem, and this in itself may create a sense of loneliness and isolation in the sufferer.

> Suddenly it's like I've come home. All these women are the same as me . . . they can't make love . . . and they are all shouting for help
> (Jan)

If you feel you would like to be part of a self help group I have listed some suggestions in the *Self Help Resource Guide* on pages 203–205.

VAGINISMIC WOMEN'S GROUP WITH PARALLEL PARTNERS GROUP

Whilst this type of group is, to my knowledge, unavailable in the United Kingdom, it nevertheless deserves mention because of its proven success in Holland. By promoting its existence I hope to generate an interest amongst us and our partners so that it may one day become available here.

For example, Dr Willeke Bezemer is one Dutch sexologist who runs women's and men's only groups, comprising eleven sessions. The discussions include four main themes:

- a woman's wish (or not) for intercourse, her sexual past, experience and upbringing, as well as her wish (or not) for a baby.

- possible benefits, if any, of having vaginismus. For example, is it concealing her lover's sexual problem; is it a way of avoiding having to tell her partner she doesn't want a baby?

- re-educating and clarifying a woman's sexuality and genitals.

- desensitization exercises to relax a woman's vagina, leading to self-exploration[*]

In many respects Dr. Bezemer's groups are very similar to those in the U.K. However, the difference is that at the final stages in the sessions[*] the partners of sufferers also share a men's only group who discuss the same issues.

POSSIBLE BENEFITS OF PARALLEL PARTNERS GROUP

Dr Bezemer finds there is not only an improvement in the couple's sexual relationship but also in their relationship generally. Women also report feeling more relaxed with higher self esteem.

One of Dr Bezemer's more important treatment goals is achieving harmony in the signals a woman makes with her body, mind and speech. That is being able to say 'Yes I want penetration and of course I can' or 'No I don't, and in that case

I can't'. Dr Bezemer calls this a 'two-sided yes' or a 'two-sided no', meaning the woman has achieved harmony.

PART III
HOW WELL DO THE TREATMENTS WORK?
WHICH TREATMENT FOR VAGINISMUS IS THE
MOST SUCCESSFUL?

About the only thing which we all have in common is the fact that we are all different; and a woman who has vaginismus will be as unique an individual as any other woman. It follows then that her response to treatment will vary too, reflecting her individuality. Statistics, however, do not reflect those differing needs and don't take into account that what works for one woman might not for another, despite the efficacy of the method.

All sorts of studies claim success in eliminating the phobia of penetration by behavioural therapy, hypnotherapy, sex therapy, psychotherapy and psychoanalysis. This establishes that ANY treatment can be successful in resolving vaginismus so long as the woman feels the therapy to be right for her particular needs. Naturally, everyone concerned in treating a spasm will want a successful and happy outcome, but I do feel that statistics claiming success rates should not be taken as an indicator of what method is best, nor should statistics determine what type of therapy a woman should choose. How is a woman going to feel, for example, if she doesn't respond well to a method that claims 100% success?

Which therapy for vaginismus? Behavioural or psychodynamic?

> I have great faith in psychotherapy . . . but it does take
> a lot of time
> (Emma)

I hope my treatment illustrations have been able to show

you the differences between, say, a behavioural and a psychodynamic method in treating vaginismus. If we think of Amy's treatment in comparison with my own, you will be able to see they are quite different.

The striking difference between behavioural and psychodynamic therapies has been cleverly described in the book *Shrinks Etc*, comparing it to a volatile situation such as fire fighting. To quote the author:

> Behavioural therapy sees itself as the fireman who pours water on the fire, while the psychodynamic therapy is the fireman who stands around and discusses how the fire started and what kind of fire it might be before rolling out his hose. Such a pragmatic viewpoint as the behavioural fireman takes may seem beguiling at first glance, but the psychodynamic fireman might respond by saying that turning on the hose before determining whether the fire is a wood or an oil blaze can have disastrous results.[25]

This example demonstrates the divide between the behavioural and psychodynamic approaches to problems. Whilst it's perfectly possible to introduce analytic technique into a behavioural method (seen in Ellen's treatment), psychoanalysts generally don't believe that behavioural methods can be integrated into their own. One of the explanations given is that an analyst who is more directive, advisory and active may upset the interflow of unspoken feelings and fantasies between he and his patient. As we saw in *Linda's Treatment*, transference is a central issue to be worked through in analysis. Analysts also see behavioural therapy as an incomplete approach because they argue that even if it changes one aspect of behaviour, vaginismus is only a small part of the problem embedded in a woman's personality. They further add that the reason why behavioural therapy so often has to be combined with counselling, hypnosis or other techniques is due to its limitations. In contrast with analysis, much of the richness of detail about a woman's past and psychology is generally not available for consideration in behavioural therapy.

However, behaviourists challenge these criticisms by saying the limitations of their method only pose a problem when trying to understand the causes behind vaginal spasm. They claim this isn't necessary to help most women overcome vaginismus. Unlike analysts, behaviourists say they only promise the woman relief from vaginismus and not any other deeper and lasting personality changes.

Although the different approaches may seem poles apart, in reality most practitioners are eclectic (using and combining each other's methods), respecting that each treatment has its own merits:

> I don't think hypnosis is the only road. I feel sure that psychoanalysis is probably a road that will lead there. It may be that one is a very enriched personality at the end of analysis. It may also be that other direct approaches miss out if one tries to produce something too intensive in a woman who has a deeper problem (Dr Anne Mathieson, Medical Hypnotherapist)

THE RESULTS

It is impossible to say categorically which treatment is better than another because there are no studies or statistics comparing one method's treatment goals with another.

As Dr Brown comments:

> I'm a bit hesitant about making comparisons because there hasn't been a good clinical trial of methods. All I know is that we (behaviourists) can help women with vaginismus. The reasons I think this particular approach works is because it's (a) about reducing the fear and (b) about the acquisition of a skill, which is true in all kinds of areas of life
> (Dr Paul Brown, Consulting Clinical Psychologist)

I haven't listed the published success rates of each method as these can be found in the literature, and I don't feel they have any real value. The choice of therapy we make should not be determined by a high statistic but by our informed knowledge and instincts.

What makes for a high success rate?

It seems the more careful the selection of sufferers, the

more successful (in terms of achieving penetration) are the results. 'Excellent' results may be achieved with a woman who, despite vaginismus, is basically healthy and has a good marriage; 'poorer' results if there is a serious personality disorder or marital conflict. Masters and Johnson's high success rates (100%) have often been attributed to the strict and careful selection of vaginismic women accepted into their treatment programme.[26] If a sufferer is chosen whose characteristics make for a successful outcome (highly motivated, with a stable relationship and no severe psychological problems) then it does not prove that the treatment is better than another. The acid test is can this high success rate still be achieved with unselected women? Isn't it like the school which only selects the brightest pupils and then reports high academic results? Does this prove the school is the best, or merely that such skilful selection of candidates ensures good results?

But what is meant by success and failure?

How should we measure and define the 'success' of a method which treats vaginismus? Is a treatment deemed successful because spasm is extinguished, or by the way a woman reports she feels, i.e. more confident, happier, able to communicate her needs etc?

Has treatment failed if vaginismus continues but there is marked improvement in a couple's relationship with renewed closeness and honest communication? Has treatment succeeded if vaginismus is resolved but our lover then goes on to experience a sexual problem?

Likewise, has treatment failed if vaginismus is not resolved during therapy, yet one year after termination spasm disappears?

> I can think of at least two cases of vaginismus where we terminated treatment and then within six months to one year the women telephoned and said 'it's better'
>
> (Dr Martin Cole, Sex Therapist)

How would this be statistically reported? As a failure or

success? And did therapy play any role in its resolution? If so, which aspects? Since figures are never what they seem all these questions need to be asked, explored and evaluated when looking at the success rates.

Most studies consider successful penetration and intercourse as the criteria for successful treatment of vaginismus, but ideally a therapist should have more individual aims, goals and outcomes for her patient. Dr Willeke Bezemer stresses that her aim is to reach harmony in a woman's verbal and bodily expression. That is, body and mind/mouth express 'Yes, I want penetration and of course I can' or 'No, I don't want penetration, and in that case of course I can't'.[27] This puts a very different light on the 100% success rates. Whilst this figure tells us women are allowing penetration, it does not confirm whether there is body and verbal harmony. For example, I felt powerless because my body would not obey my orders . . . I felt it cheated me. On the one hand I spoke 'I want penetration' yet on the other my body said 'No, I don't want penetration'. I also felt my mouth deceived me since my body expressed my feelings honestly whereas my speech did not.[28] It is therefore important that the goal of therapy be to reach a harmonious integration of speech, body and conscious mind.

This is an area of conflict and difficulty for most women, not just those who suffer from vaginismus.

IS THERE ANYTHING WE CAN DO TO INFLUENCE THE SUCCESS OF A TREATMENT?

There are no hard and fast rules which will definitely guarantee a successful outcome, but there are factors (conscious and unconscious) which may come into play that can either help or hinder the process. In reality it's only if we continue to express purely negative attitudes that success is less likely, and the boundaries between hindering and helping will inevitably be blurred. It will therefore be quite natural at times to have a combination of feelings which may both enhance and obstruct the therapeutic process.

Helping the process

Any therapeutic experience may be greatly enhanced if the woman comes of her own accord, is highly motivated, prepared to work hard and endure a certain amount of pain. Naturally, such aspects need to be equally matched in her therapist. The practitioners all stress the importance of a trusting relationship between the sufferer and themselves. Motivation is also cited as being an important factor. One doctor adds how important it is that the woman's partner be loving and supportive. Generally, the outcome is felt to be more favourable if:-

THE THERAPIST:

- has a capacity to understand our feelings.
- is skilled, sensitive, intuitive and patient.

IF THERE IS:

- mutual trust
- willingness to confront our pain yet acknowledge our fears.
- motivation to change and to grow.
- support from people and the environment.

AND IF WE ARE:

- willing to ask for support.
- able to express ourselves lovingly and enjoy intimacy.
- seeking help primarily to overcome vaginismus and not because of the wish for a baby.
- able to participate in the healing process and take responsibility where appropriate.
- open to success.

Hindering the process

One doctor explained that success may be impeded if the

woman doesn't feel safe enough to let go of her controls, similar to an intimate partnership she may have.

A therapist working psychoanalytically says that the partner's unconscious conflicts can also interfere with our progress:

> It could be that he's satisfied with the situation as it is, so that if the woman becomes more receptive and relaxed and things begin to shift in an internal way, it mightn't suit him
> (Jill Curtis, Psychotherapist)

Dr Brown cited levels of fear that he can't get underneath as impeding successful outcome. He then explained how the path of therapy may be obstructed by outside influences:

> One of the most difficult and unsuccessful attempts at treating vaginismus was where a priest was giving my client directly contrary advice at the same time
> (Dr Paul Brown, Consulting Clinical Psychologist)

For sex therapist Dr Cole, it is a lack of knowledge about the true causes of vaginismus which may prevent him from intervening and may lead him to use the wrong approach for that particular woman.

The outcome is accordingly felt to be less favourable if:-

THE THERAPIST

– lacks skills, sensitivity and ability to empathize.

IF WE:

– remain ambivalent about confronting our problem.

– continue to resist change.

– only seek help because of external pressures.

– enter therapy because we feel humiliated that we are virgins rather than because we wish to enjoy intimacy.

– lack motivation.

- don't believe we can change or grow.

- feel negative towards ourselves, towards treatment, our partner and our therapist.

- continue to put up strong defences.

- remain unable to recognise and make use of inter-pretations and insights.

- are unable to work with our fantasies as they seem so real, can't distinguish them from reality and therefore can't give them up.

- continue to see the relationship with our therapist as a struggle for power and control.

- continue to try and undermine the therapist's impact.

- continue to intellectualize, deny, withhold conscious thoughts and feelings and repress relevant material.

- remain passive with no real engagement in the therapeutic relationship.

- continue to place entire responsibility for change upon the therapist.

- remain fearful of intimacy, dependency, trust and loss of control.

- remain closed to success.

THE TREATMENTS: A PERSONAL VIEW

I include this very personal assessment of the treatments for the following reasons: firstly, I wish to help women understand that there is no one or right road to successfully resolving vaginismus. However, I believe some women need to know this from a sufferer's first-hand experience, not just from a clinician's statistic: both are valid.

Secondly, in being candid about the ways in which certain methods were inappropriate for me I hope to enable women to consider the appropriateness of each treatment themselves rather than leaving their choice automatically in the hands of an 'expert'. In showing how and why a particular method didn't work for me, and in making personal observations about it, I hope to support the woman who may have difficulty in finding the right treatment and to show that it's OK if her first attempts don't succeed.

Thirdly, much of women's pain, experiences and history tend to go unnoticed in the world. Consequently, I don't want to suppress the way in which some doctors treated me, despite my wish not to offend the entire medical profession. I want other women to know that if this also happened to them it wasn't necessarily their fault, but perhaps more to do with the doctor's unconscious conflicts combined with their own.

Understanding the causes

Rather than inventing more and more cures and treatments to resolve vaginismus there should be increasing concentration placed upon *how* and *why* a woman has developed vaginismus in the first place, leaving aside new ways of trying to penetrate her. If we don't view vaginismus solely as a sexual problem, the obvious treatments will be ones which explore our psychology. Whilst I tend to favour psychodynamic as opposed to strictly behavioural approaches, I am not in any way dismissing the value of the behavioural method. As we have seen, the practitioners I spoke with are all aware of the need to explore underlying conflicts rather than just employ methods to stretch our vaginas and alter our behaviour. What I can't understand or support is the method which doesn't allow for the possibility of examining in our own time and way what the spasm is protecting and defending against. This is also felt by Frances:

> I feel quite irate about the sub-Masters-&-Johnson-cum-behavioural approach which inevitably suggests that sensate focusing and the use of dilators and fingers will solve the problem in much the same automatic way that a pipe can be unblocked! I've never had any problem putting my fingers in my vagina, yet I still suffer from vaginismus
> (Frances)

The move away from sexual methods

My concern and cautiousness about direct approaches may be unfounded in certain cases. For example, if a woman's difficulties occurred during later development but she has successfully negotiated the earlier phases, then behavioural therapy may well suit her. It may be able to give her the 'green light' to go ahead and now embark on sexuality. However, there may be drawbacks in this approach for the sufferer whose troubles date from a much earlier stage in her development. Whilst she may well be able to function sexually after treatment, she might still be unable to feel loved, and continue to feel terrible deep down inside.

If the pressure is removed from the goal of penetration this can allow us to choose more easily a method which explores underlying conflicts, since we won't feel dominated or pressurized by the sexual aspects of our symptom. It isn't always appropriate or necessary to treat vaginismus with a sexual therapy because it's inaccurate to separate our sexual relationships from others. The issues of basic trust and allowing others into our true selves are pervasive of EVERY relationship we have, not just the sexual ones. It's possible to know about a woman's sexuality simply by being aware of her interactions with others, without the subject of sex being raised at all.

After much thought, research and discussions with sufferers and specialists, I remain unconvinced that one can simply by-pass the deeper underlying conflicts of vaginismus and deal only with alleviating the presenting symptom. As *Surgery* shows, there may very well be a shift of symptoms meaning spasm leaves our vaginas but shifts elsewhere. I'm not alone in believing vaginismus to be developmental and that psychotherapy is the most appropriate form of treatment. This, too, was the conclusion of *Virgin Wives*.

> It was only psychotherapy that enabled me to solve the problem . . . the dilators would have been useless without it
> (Emma)

However, as one psychoanalyst pointed out to me, some

women don't 'take' to therapy at first and may need to go through the disappointment and failure of the physical approaches. There is an unconscious resistance in all of us to looking inside ourselves, and this is reflected in our reticence to enter the therapies which require us to do this.

A review of literature may reappraise treatments

Both past and contemporary publications appear to heavily influence the treatments for vaginismus. Pre-feminist literature often refers to us as 'hostile' or 'infantile' and this view has mainly come about because the psychological measure of adulthood is genitally-related, i.e. whether or not we are able to allow penetration. If we remove the focus from the vagina it will not only produce a shift in the way we are viewed, but also our partner is unlikely to be judged in terms of his masculinity or potency. Current approaches to sexual problems also appear to be too focused on the genitals. Whilst it's true many sexual problems manifest in one's vagina or penis, this may miss the origins of where the difficulty truly lies. For example, vaginismus has as much – or as little – to do with the vagina as anorexia nervosa has to do with the mouth.

We can create changes within our own treatments

As there may well be cultural, religious and ethnic influences which come into play in the makeup of our psychology, I feel it appropriate to set our psychology in the context of our social background when exploring vaginismus. I arrive at this conclusion since noticing and wondering why the incidence of vaginismus appears much higher amongst women in Ireland, where there are strict religious taboos. An awareness of how class and race can affect both a therapist and his views of a sufferer also needs to be developed. If our therapist remains blind to such issues he may 'psychologize' rather than explore them with us.

By including these aspects I hope to stimulate a dialogue within the treatments for vaginismus between every woman and her doctor/therapist. The methods by which we currently treat vaginismus unconsciously reflect the way vaginal spasm is seen: this is true for most problems and treatments. There needs to be more space and support for practitioners to explore, understand, identify with and ultimately bring compassion to the way a sufferer is seen and treated. Only then can these elements be reflected in the way our vaginismus is clinically treated and generally responded to.

PART IV
WHERE ARE THE TREATMENTS AVAILABLE?

The treatment of vaginismus is available both within the National Health Service and outside it, i.e. in private medicine. However, because sexual problems and psychotherapy in general tend not to be considered priorities, waiting lists in the health service may be long and equally the amount of time allocated to a woman might often fall short of what may be necessary. If treatment isn't available or satisfactory within the health service then you shouldn't necessarily be deterred from seeking help privately. Whilst this treatment isn't free, fees can often be negotiable depending upon your financial circumstances.

The term 'psychosexual' used in the context of treating vaginismus simply describes a method concerned with the psychological as opposed to physical aspects of sex, though it appears to be an umbrella term used to describe various methods of treating sexual problems and may not define any one particular method.

Most private therapies tend to be based mainly in the large cities, and waiting lists are generally shorter than those in the health service. Hopefully, as the need for psychotherapy becomes more acknowledged then access to these facilities will become more widespread nationally.

Though I am unable to personally recommend any particular doctor, clinic or treatment you are free to use my suggestions as a guide. As explained in Chapter Four, I feel it always advisable to contact therapists via their respective professional associations, thus ensuring that they will be a member of a recognised body and thereby governed by standards and codes of professional ethics.*

TREATMENTS WITHIN THE NATIONAL HEALTH SERVICE

The General Practitioner

> I think more GPs than used to be are alert to the idea of treating vaginismus other than by medical intervention
> (Dr Paul Brown, Consulting Clinical Psychologist)

Whilst most family doctors are sympathetic, it should be recognised that the majority aren't sufficiently trained, nor do they have the time, to offer treatment for vaginismus themselves. You may, of course, be one of the lucky ones whose GP has undertaken training with the Institute of Psychosexual Medicine, or perhaps is a medical hypnotist or has counselling skills. If so, he will be able to offer you treatment, providing you wish to work with him.

Despite lack of funds there are increasing numbers of general practitioners receiving a training in psychosexual medicine. The advantage of treating vaginismus at the primary care level is that it may be dealt with when it first presents early on, before becoming very reinforced. For example, vaginismus may first present in a very young woman asking for contraception. If the GP has difficulties in giving her a smear test it's at this point he would be able to take up the significance of her difficulty and be able to explore and work with her.

Since early diagnosis and help with vaginal spasm may prevent a woman from seeking inappropriate help, I feel it important that as many general practitioners as possible

---

* Although I list each organisation, this does not in any way imply a specific recommendation. I am unable to accept responsibility for how each member of these organisations may deal with your problem.

receive training in psychosexual medicine. As Alison Clegg explains, a GP may be a woman's only contact:

> The GP very often can be the first person a woman approaches for help. If a woman receives no help from her GP she may feel unable ever again to ask for help from anyone else
> (Alison Clegg, Sex Therapy Training Officer, National Marriage Guidance Council)

However, if your general practitioner is unable to treat you, then a consultation with him should result in a referral to one of the following:-

Psychotherapy & psychosexual treatment in hospitals and Family Planning clinics

Most large hospitals run psychosexual clinics, and although it will vary the treatment generally offered is sex therapy based upon a modified less intense version of Masters and Johnson. The service is free, works on an appointments system and is similar to attending an outpatients clinic. You may also telephone the Departments of Psychology or Psychiatry in your nearest general hospital and ask whether they have either a 'Sexual Dysfunction' or a 'Psychosexual' clinic.

Psychosexual sessions may also be held in a few birth control clinics run by the Family Planning Association. Because of financial cut backs in the health service the availability of services cannot be relied upon. Therefore, in order to locate the nearest clinic offering this treatment you are advised in the first instance to contact the Family Planning Information Service, 27 Mortimer Street, London W1N 7RJ on 01-636 7866 and ask for Clinic Enquiries. They may also be able to advise whether any Vaginismus Groups are being run in hospitals.

INSTITUTE OF PSYCHOSEXUAL MEDICINE

11 Chandos Street, Cavendish Square, London W1M 9DE.
Tel: 01-580 0631
Members are GPs and doctors who have been specifically

trained to develop their skills to treat vaginismus and other psychosexual problems. They have been passed and approved by a Panel at the Institute. Upon receipt of a stamped addressed envelope a list of doctors in your area will be forwarded on request. This will include those who practise both in the health service and privately.

ASSOCIATION OF SEXUAL & MARITAL THERAPISTS

P.O. Box 62, Sheffield, S10 3TS. Tel: 0742-303901.
Promotes standards of therapy, training and research into marital and sexual problems. Members come from varied disciplines of psychology, medicine, counselling, nursing and education. Upon receipt of a stamped addressed envelope a list of NHS clinics in your area where qualified sex therapists practise will be forwarded to you.

THE TAVISTOCK CLINIC

120 Belsize Lane, London NW3 5BA. Tel: 01-435 7111.
National Health Service unit so treatment is free, but clinic's catchment area is North London and North East Thames Region only. Psychotherapy as opposed to sexual therapy is generally offered.

BIRMINGHAM WOMEN'S COUNSELLING & THERAPY CENTRE

43 Ladywood Middleway, Birmingham B16 8HA. Tel: 021-455 8677.
Self-referral, but catchment area is Central Birmingham Health District only. Offers individual therapy and counselling from a feminist perspective. Initial assessment offered. Treatment is free.

BROOK ADVISORY CENTRES:

Central Office: 153A East Street, London S.E.17. Tel: 01-708 1234.
Self-referral. Service generally offered for women under 25

years of age. Some Centres impose strict age limits but others don't, so it's best to check first. Generally the service is free but, again, some Centres may charge fees for counselling. As well as treating vaginismus they provide free birth control. Contact Central Referrals Secretary for centre nearest your home.

BRITISH ASSOCIATION FOR COUNSELLING

37A Sheep Street, Rugby, Warks CV21 3BX.
Registered charity whose aims are to promote awareness of counselling throughout the U.K. and maintain and raise standards of practice. Enquiries cannot be dealt with by telephone, but if you send a stamped addressed envelope a list of therapists, both in the NHS and private sector, will be sent.

Vaginismus Group Therapy:

As explained, due to financial cutbacks the availability is limited. However, your GP, the Family Planning Association or National Marriage Guidance Council (page 199) may be able to advise if any groups are run in certain hospitals. Letter of referral from GP is required.

Psychoanalysis:

THE LONDON CLINIC OF PSYCHOANALYSIS

63 New Cavendish Street, London W1M 7RD. Tel: 01-580 4952/3
Because demand for analysis is greater than the number of available analysts there are only a limited number of sessions available within the NHS or at reduced fees. Because of limited number of places, there is a careful assessment procedure. Since analysis doesn't dwell on the symptom the assessment is not based upon what kind of problem you have but rather the commitment and motivation to attend five times weekly for at least two years. GP may contact clinic direct.

SOUTHERN IRELAND:
CATHOLIC MARRIAGE ADVISORY COUNCIL

All Hallows College, Drumcondra, Dublin 9. Tel: Dublin 371151.
Able to advise on sexual therapy in Southern Ireland for vaginismus.

NORTHERN IRELAND:
CATHOLIC MARRIAGE ADVISORY COUNCIL

Cana House, 56 Lisburn Road, Belfast BT9 6AF. Tel: Belfast 233002.
Able to advise on sexual therapy in Northern Ireland for vaginismus. Belfast City & Tyrone Fermanna Hospitals currently run psychosexual clinics.

MARRIAGE GUIDANCE COUNCIL:

Tel: Belfast 323454.
Able to offer sexual therapy for vaginismus. Can also refer to psychosexual clinics at nearby hospitals, if required.

TREATMENTS OUTSIDE THE NATIONAL HEALTH SERVICE

The following offer treatment in the private sector and may be contacted direct. A letter from your GP may not always be required, but in some instances it may be necessary for him/her to know of the treatment you are receiving. Fees vary and some may be negotiable.

GENERAL PRACTITIONER

Subject to treatment being affordable, your GP may be able to recommend a clinic or therapist. If not, the following may be contacted:

Psychosexual & Sex Therapy:

INSTITUTE OF PSYCHOSEXUAL MEDICINE

(Details on page 195)

ASSOCIATION OF SEXUAL & MARITAL THERAPISTS

(Details on page 196)

NATIONAL MARRIAGE GUIDANCE COUNCIL

Head Office: Herbert Gray College, Little Church Street, Rugby, Warwickshire. Tel: 0788-73241.
Offers help for wide range of problems, including vaginismus, and many branches now have specialised sex therapy counsellors. Fees are negotiable, with waiting lists likely in London and some of the clinics outside London.
Look in local telephone directory for nearest branch.

Counselling:

BIRMINGHAM BROOK ADVISORY CENTRE.

Tel: 021-455 0491.
One of Brook's Centres which does not have an age limit. Initial assessment offered but fees are negotiable.

BRITISH ASSOCIATION FOR COUNSELLING

(Details on page 197)

JEWISH MARRIAGE COUNCIL

23 Ravenshurst Avenue, London NW4 4EL. Tel: 01-203 6311.
Runs a confidential counselling service for marital, family and personal problems and is sensitive and understanding of Jewish cultural aspects. Working within this particular framework they are able to be aware and sympathetic to problems which vaginismus may create within a marital relationship. Fees are negotiable.

Hypnotherapy:

BRITISH SOCIETY OF MEDICAL & DENTAL HYPNOSIS

42 Links Road, Ashstead, Surrey, KT21 2HJ. Tel: 03722–73522.
Membership limited to doctors and dentists only and if you contact the Referrals Secretary, Mrs Samuels, a list of practitioners will be forwarded. Letter of ï :ferral is always required from your GP.

BRITISH SOCIETY OF EXPERIMENTAL & CLINICAL HYPNOSIS

Dr Michael Heap, c/o Department of Psychology, Middlewood Hospital, Sheffield S6 1TP. Tel: 0742-85222.
Membership is limited to doctors, psychologists, dentists and psychotherapists. Contact Dr. Heap enclosing stamped addressed envelope for list of practitioners in your area. Depending upon where you live, he may be able to refer you to a hypnotist with expertise in treating vaginismus. Letter of referral from GP required.

INSTITUTE OF ANALYTICAL HYPNOTHERAPISTS

P.O. Box 180, Bournemouth, Dorset BH8 8NH. Tel: 0202-304624.
Members of this Institute have followed a Course of training in Psychotherapy, Analysis and Hypnosis which enables them to specialise in 'Hypno-Analytical' Therapy. Enquiries may be made in writing or by telephone for referral to a practitioner in your area.

THE SOCIETY FOR PRIMARY CAUSE ANALYSIS BY HYPNOSIS

13 Beechwood Road, Sanderstead, South Croydon, Surrey CR2 OAE. Tel: 01-657 3624.
P.C.A. therapy is based on a concept pioneered in New Zealand whereby the technique of regressive analysis is used in conjunction with hypnosis. At present, most members of this Society only practise in or around London, and referrals may be made by telephoning or writing, enclosing a stamped addressed envelope.

Psychotherapy & Psychoanalysis:

BRITISH ASSOCIATION OF PSYCHOTHERAPISTS

121 Hendon Lane, London N3 3PR. Tel: 01-346 1747.
One of the few professional bodies in the U.K. which trains and qualifies psychotherapists according to agreed standards. Consultation offered with experienced psychotherapist to discuss whether it would be an appropriate form of help and treatment. Orientation of therapists is psychoanalytic covering Freudian, Jungian and Kleinian concepts. Although majority of members are in London they will endeavour to refer you to someone in your area. Fees for regular treatment are negotiated between patient and therapist. Enquiries may be made in writing to the referrals secretary enclosing a stamped addressed envelope.

WOMEN'S THERAPY CENTRE

6 Manor Gardens, London N7 6LA. Tel: 01-263 6200.
Co-founded by therapists Luise Eichenbaum and Susie Orbach in 1976, the Centre's philosophy is woman-orientated, offering therapy and group workshops from a feminist perspective. To arrange for assessment write to them enclosing a stamped addressed envelope.

WOMEN'S COUNSELLING & THERAPY SERVICE

Top Floor, Oxford Chambers, Oxford Place, Leeds LS1 3AX. Tel: 0532-455725.
Offers therapy in the Leeds Metropolitan District only. Publicly-funded but donations are encouraged and there may be a waiting list. Offers analytic-groups though not specifically for vaginismus.

Psychoanalysis:

SOCIETY OF ANALYTICAL PSYCHOLOGY

1 Daleham Gardens, London NW3 5TB. Tel: 01-435 7696.

Members trained in analytical psychology, many are doctors. Majority practise in London, but SAP will try to refer you to someone in your area. To arrange initial assessment, contact Referrals Secretary in writing, enclosing a stamped addressed envelope.

Group Therapy:

For professional reasons laid down by the General Medical Council I am unable to include the addresses of doctors offering group analysis. This is because it may be regarded by the British Medical Association as advertising, which its members are forbidden to do. If you wish to take part in a group such as Diane and Tim's in Chapter Five, either consult your GP or contact the author c/o the publisher.

Sexuality Group:

REDWOOD WOMEN'S TRAINING ASSOCIATION

Head Office: 'Invergarry', Kitlings Lane, Walton-on-the-Hill, Stafford, ST17 OLE. Tel: 0785-662823 Maggie Mitchell
Provides courses in assertiveness and sexuality, enabling women to find their strengths, grow in confidence and value themselves. The philosophy of Redwood is non-competitive and committed to non-sexist and non-racist principles. Sexuality Groups run for eight to ten weeks (a two-hourly session each week or for one or two full days). A list of names and addresses of groups in your area (throughout England & Wales) will be sent to you by contacting Maggie Mitchell.

Homoeopathy & Alternative Therapies

BRITISH HOMOEOPATHIC ASSOCIATION

27A Devonshire Street, London W1N 1RJ. Tel: 01-935 2163.
Lists doctors who practise homoeopathic medicine, hospitals and NHS and non-NHS clinics.

SOCIETY OF HOMOEOPATHS

47 Canada Grove, Bognor Regis, West Sussex PO21 1DW. Tel: 0243-860678.

Has a register of professional homoeopaths who have graduated after four years training and six months clinical assessment. Send stamped addressed envelope for list of nearest practitioners.

INSTITUTE OF COMPLEMENTARY MEDICINE

21 Portland Place, London W1N 3AF.

If you would like advice on which 'alternative' therapist to choose for vaginismus you may write (enclosing a stamped addressed envelope) to 'Information Service', the ICM's referral service.

SELF-HELP RESOURCE GUIDE

Even during therapy there may be times when we feel isolated and lonely. Whilst these feelings can, of course, be explored and shared with our therapist they may nonetheless remain painful reminders of our sense of exclusion from the sexually-active world. Because many of us including me, have suffered alone, it has made me realise the importance of meeting other sufferers. I have therefore put together some suggestions of places to contact. The list is not exhaustive and centres mainly on London, but I hope it may lead to further contacts closer to home. Not all suggestions relate to self-help groups, but more to general health-related issues concerning women.

BIRMINGHAM WOMEN'S COUNSELLING & THERAPY CENTRE

(Details on page 196)

As well as a counselling service they will initiate the setting up of a self-help group if requested.

LIFELINE,

P.O. Box 251, Marlborough, Wiltshire SN8 1EA. Tel: 079373-286

An organisation which helps sexually and physically abused women and offers support and self-help sexual groups as well as its own magazine (published quarterly). This can act as a useful contact source for vaginismus sufferers.

NATIONAL ASSOCIATION FOR THE CHILDLESS

Birmingham Settlement, 318 Summer Lane, Birmingham B19 3RL. Tel: 021-359 4887/2113.
Registered charity and self-help organisation for childless people, concerned with the feelings of those who can't have children. The NAC help each other with the various problems encountered by the infertile and although vaginismus does not cause medical infertility it can nevertheless result in childlessness. Send small contribution for membership and stamped addressed envelope for self-help group in your area. NAC also publishes a newsletter exchanging information and experiences.

WINVISIBLE (WOMEN WITH VISIBLE & INVISIBLE DISABILITIES)

King's Cross Women's Centre, 71 Tonbridge Street, London WC1H 9DZ. Tel: 01-837 7509
WinVisible is a network of black and white women with visible and invisible disabilities, and a member of the International Wages for Housework Campaign. They are campaigning for economic independence, political and social autonomy, mobility, access and housing, against welfare cuts, racism, rape and military-industrial pollution. If you are able to form a local self-help group and need meeting space then WinVisible would be happy to discuss your requirements with the author. Please contact me first via the publisher.

WOMEN'S COUNSELLING & THERAPY SERVICE, LEEDS.

(Details on page 196)
Offers initial advice only to set up a self-help group.

WOMEN & MEDICAL PRACTICE, 666 High Rd, London N17 OAB. Tel: 01-885 2277

Women's health collective committed to compaigning against all forms of oppression which may be encountered in the course of medical treatments. As well as offering one-to-one counselling they provide a list of alternative practitioners and register of local and national Women's Centres, Women's Groups and health-related organisations. Would be a valuable contact for self-help group or workshop since one of their members might be prepared to take part in the group. Runs Newsletter.

WOMEN'S THERAPY CENTRE

(Details on page 201)
Offers workshops, groups and advice on self-help covering all women's issues. Two Vaginismus Workshops have been held during 1983 and 1984.
Further suggestions for creating self-help and support groups:

- Place cards in local feminist bookshops and women's centres.

- Write article/letter requesting other vaginismus sufferers to contact you. Some of the organisations listed here print their own newsletters/bulletins and would be happy to hear from you.

CHAPTER SIX

Can Vaginismus Be Prevented?

I don't see how we can prevent vaginismus because we're back to there being one cause . . . if you do this to your child it'll cause vaginismus or if you don't do this it won't
(Jill Curtis, Psychotherapist)

Psychological damage may be difficult to foresee

I wondered and wondered, is it possible to prevent the occurrence of vaginismus? Since understanding the origins of my vaginal spasm I've asked myself if this knowledge might be used to prevent its occurrence in, say, a daughter of my own. Whilst there's growing emphasis on preventive medicine, it doesn't automatically follow that we can prevent psychological damage in a growing child as easily as we can lessen the dangers of physical harm (such as by keeping poisons out of reach and teaching our children how to cross the road). Life is a continuum from birth to death, and no matter how important certain events are there is never just *one* incident that causes anything. People who experience trauma in early life can often lead very happy existences if positive influences follow to counteract the negative ones. Therefore, it shouldn't be automatically assumed that our insensitivity or natural errors when raising our children will definitely cause vaginismus or any emotional problem. Other factors should always be considered, such as the inherent emotional makeup of children and their own particular needs.

Realistically there is little anyone can actively do to

prevent the onset of vaginismus. Thinking back to Chapter Three there is probably a limit to how much good mothering can prevent or alter the phantasies a baby has ... phantasies which may be influential in the development of vaginismus. This is because they develop before an infant is able to make rational judgements about external events or her parents' behaviour towards her. Whilst it's true that mother plays a vital role in providing a secure environment if a baby's true, not hidden, psychological self is to develop, she is in no way responsible for the development of spasm since it's never caused by her knowingly 'doing' something to her baby. As one therapist explains:

> Parents can't prevent vaginismus because most try consciously to be good parents. They are all the time carrying their own lives, their own mothers and fathers with them
> (Marianne Granö, Sexual Psychotherapist, Sweden)

To say vaginismus cannot be prevented may seem rather pessimistic, but if we look at prevention within a much wider framework then the possibilities open up. For example, trying to prevent an unconscious interaction between infant and parent, needs to be seen more in terms of understanding how and why sexual and emotional problems arise, rather than trying to prevent or cure them.

Understanding and awareness may be the key to prevention

Growing awareness, knowledge and openness about the causes and existence of vaginismus may help to raise the consciousness of parents, alerting them to the importance of sensitivity in their interactions with their children. Even quite simple insights into a child's psychological life can help us to understand how crucial early emotional experiences are, and their impact on shaping our futures.

Most parents want to do the best for their children. Unfortunately, there are so many ways of harming a child, and it can be done unintentionally and unconsciously. It's often easier for us, through fear, ignorance and social conditioning to hold our children back than it is to help them reach their full potential. Instead of blaming others, it might be more positive to accept the difficulties in being a parent and acknowledge that most mistakes can usually be repaired with love and understanding as well as accepting our responsibilities. The suggestions in this chapter aren't intended as a 'Guide to Good Parenting', since none of the points made either on their own or combined can definitely prevent the occurrence of vaginismus. However, increased consciousness and thought might lessen the possibilities. There is no such thing as a 'perfect' parent, and strange as it may seem if we are too perfect we actually run the risk of being too good a parent. Donald Winnicott points out that problems can arise when mothers are so experienced at reading their children's needs that they anticipate everything in advance and thus unwittingly rob their children of the experience of disappointment and gaining control for themselves.[1] We need somehow to maintain that difficult balance between wanting to satisfy our children totally, yet realising this is neither realistically possible nor even healthy.

THE FAMILY'S ROLE

A child's view of the adult

Perhaps more useful than reading child-rearing manuals is a parent's ability to 'become' the child, to feel a child's feelings and to see things from their perspective. If we understand that a girl feels ambivalent towards mother because mother is the source of both her happiness and her pain, then we can more easily allow that child the expression of negative and hateful feelings, as well as the loving ones.

We need to recognise and be more sensitive to a child's awareness of adult relationships and sexuality. Psychoanalysis confirms that the 'primal scene' may all too easily be misinterpreted, leading to erroneous assumptions which arise out of intense unconscious feelings of exclusion. If such a situation isn't handled thoughtfully, an infant may be left feeling unable to compete with mother, instilling a sense of terror should she try to trespass on mother's sexual territory by competing for father's love.

However hard it may be to accept, we need to acknowledge that even very small children may have unconscious incestuous feelings and fantasies about their parents. Similarly, parents may also experience unconscious erotic feelings towards their children. By acknowledging to ourselves that this is a natural process, it allows a child to mature without undue guilt or anxiety. However, this doesn't give licence to parents to overtly question children about such feelings, or to act upon any desires they might have themselves. This is a process which goes on inside a child's unconscious which should be left there to nurture quietly, free from inappropriate intrusion. Likewise, parents should never act seductively or respond to seductiveness from a child. More difficult is finding a way to ensure that children don't interpret the latter as rejection.

Another important aspect of the parent-child relationship is the boundary which must exist between them. For the adult this involves acting within a responsible framework, not imposing sexual or emotional demands upon our children, nor expecting our needs to be met by them. For the child it's simply the reassurance of knowing the relationship with her parents is clearly defined, relieving her of any anxieties she might have about crossing boundaries. She is then able to happily engage in childhood rather than become prematurely involved, occupied or confused by the demands of adults.

Dr Brown highlights the importance of this aspect:

> The family's role is knowing how to be both private and relaxed about sex, and how to have boundaries around important issues like one's sexual development
>
> (Dr Paul Brown, Consulting Clinical Psychologist)

Self-image, self-love and self-worth

It needs to be recognised that origins of poor self-esteem, lack of worth and self-love, and a negative self-image can often be traced to unsupportive, unpraising and dismissive attitudes towards a child from its parents. These early feelings of ugliness, unimportance and self-loathing may later re-emerge, making it impossible, for example, for a woman to open up and share with others her true self, including vaginismus.

Since early detection of problems is always preferable to unnoticed ones continuing beyond adolescence, we need to be acutely aware of any anxieties that our children are consistently transmitting.

Positive attitudes communicated to children about sex and their bodies can go towards promoting healthy growth without undue fear of sex.

> If a girl is deprived of understanding and touching her vagina, it may build up into a psychological barrier that she mustn't do it
> (Barbara Lamb, Nurse Psychosexual Counsellor)

If parents feel comfortable and at ease with their own sexuality, then they are more likely to transmit positive messages to their children about sex.

A recent survey in a woman's magazine revealed that little girls whose fathers are accessible rather than distant are more likely to be orgasmic and enjoy their sexuality.[2] This demonstrates that 'being there' for one's child is not only very important for her psychological welfare but also her sexual development.

An infant's need to feel loved and secure

We don't live in an ideal world, but whenever possible we should avoid leaving baby unattended for unreasonably long periods to cry alone. This may instill a sense of isolation, unhappiness, loneliness and insecurity, leading her to expect that nobody will ever come to relieve her of her misery. This may then result in her subsequently mistrusting and hating the entire world, seeing it as being hostile, insecure and cruelly withholding.

Women who encourage independence in their children because they feel relatively secure and fulfilled generally fare better as mothers than those who are emotionally troubled or immature. Unresolved conflicts in a woman's personality combined with social factors may result in her needing her baby to boost her ego, making it difficult for a child to separate psychologically from mother. This inability to separate and ultimately own one's vagina is particularly noticeable in women who go on to develop vaginismus.

Mother not seen as the expert

Whilst it's commonly recognised how essential mother is to her infant, paradoxically she is not considered to be the expert on her baby. This leads to our being encouraged to draw upon outside expertise in the form of books and professionals. It's hardly surprising that women come to feel insecure and shaky about whether their responses to baby are the 'right' ones. Perhaps we need to be encouraged more to trust our own feelings and not rely exclusively on textbook manuals or others.

> On the one hand motherhood is deified . . . and on the other hand it is undermined
> (Susie Orbach, Psychotherapist)

Out of insecurity and a desire to be model parents, many of us rely on rigid feeding schedules rather than spontaneous and intuitive responses to baby's oral and emotional needs. This may lead to a child not feeling special, nor as having unique qualities which need attending to in a unique way. If we aren't encouraged to be imaginative and see children as individuals, we may forget they are 'real' and be quite clumsy and unintentionally brutal in our handling of them. This can lead to a child's expectation that the world is clumsy, is somehow not to be trusted. It can take a long time to renounce such a belief and trust others.

Whilst parents-to-be are inundated with books and instructions on how to breathe through contractions and how to feed and change baby, there is very little emphasis or guidance about the emotional lives of parent and child. There may often be no psychological sense in many adults of what goes on for baby throughout her emotional development, so the education of parents, teachers, nursery workers and childminders needs to be reappraised. Without this kind of knowledge and discussion, the language of psychology may remain a jargon of the informed or elite. To help remedy this, ante-natal classes need to include information not just about nappy-changing but also the emotional aspects of child rearing:

> A parent needs to have a sense of her own emotional life as an adult in order to be receptive to the potential emotional life of her infant
> (Susie Orbach, Psychotherapist)

Becoming a parent re-evokes the baby we once were

In the same way that a therapist can't be taught how to feel and be intuitive, so too parents cannot learn awareness and sensitivity simply from psychoanalytic 'lessons'. Instead, we need to be helped to understand that it isn't only what we do to our children, but how we feel at the time of doing it which matters. For example, many of us may be unaware just how sensitive baby is to the emotional attitudes of her caregivers. For this reason, it's far better to have a relaxed happy mother feeding to a schedule as opposed to an anxious and resentful one who breastfeeds on demand.

When problems arise in the way a parent relates intimately to her infant, they usually spring from unconscious emotional conflicts which stem from the mother's own childhood. When a woman becomes a mother, powerful emotions are re-evoked which have a great deal in common with feelings stirred up in her by her parents and siblings when she herself was a child. The way she feels towards baby is often distorted by unconscious early conflicts she re-experiences, leading her to perhaps respond in inappropriate ways. However, the difficulty isn't in this recurrance of feelings, which all of us experience as parents, but rather in a mother's or father's inability to understand, recognise, tolerate and control such ambivalent feelings.[3] Much guilt and confusion could be alleviated were we helped to understand and recognise that our own needy, possibly deprived, baby inside us is always recreated when we give birth ourselves.

Healing inequalities between mother, father and baby
When discussing prevention with Susie Orbach she explained how she sees vaginismus as being no different from other psychological symptoms. In other words, it is really about difficulties in how to relate intimately, and the terror and desire that that produces. Part of prevention would be in changing the cultural atmosphere around the whole issue of intimacy:

> We are illiterate when it comes to intimate relationships, so we need to change the illiteracy of emotional contact rather than simply introduce procedures to 'deal with' or 'prevent' vaginismus (Susie Orbach, Psychotherapist)

It then follows that issues surrounding the way we relate intimately need to be understood and explored. Since the all-important figure at the start of life is usually mother, perhaps it's here we can create change. Are there ways to help limit the conditions which make it ripe for vaginismus to develop?

In the book *What Do Women Want?*, the authors suggest that changing the position of women in society will help change the psychological makeup of women.[4] This requires involving men equally in child-rearing to alter men's psychology. As nurturers men will experience the same feelings of inadequacy, anxiety and vulnerability that women currently experience.

The results of this might be:-

- dependency no longer being seen as signifying weakness.

- our needs for contact, care, intimacy and love will be accepted as natural.

- two parents of different genders can help baby tolerate painful experiences and so make her feel she can survive them, that they aren't dangerous, overwhelming or ugly.

- all badness and distrust will no longer derive from experiences of disappointment with mothers/women (the root of misogyny in male psychology?) because both good and bad experiences will now be associated with both parents.

SOCIETY'S ROLE

Apart from the family, what can we as a society collectively do to reduce the occurrence and stigma of vaginismus?

A healthy sexual climate

We need to encourage a climate where sex and intimacy are expressed, not just openly, but without derision, shame, or embarrassment, respecting its specialness and sacredness. Ways in which such a climate might be created are:

- recognition that sex needs to be seen within a more holistic framework. This means integrating our sexuality in with the other aspects of ourselves, rather than separating it. Separation of sex removes it from the 'whole' persons we are, leading to its compartmentalization, where we put sex in one box and love in another. Such divisions reinforce women being seen as property, sex as a commodity, or the use of sex as a male weapon against women to dominate and oppress them.

- acknowledgement that sex is the deepest expression of human creativity and communication, and consequently emotions of such depth and complexity might well result in the enormous pain often surrounding sexuality. Unresolved pain around intimacy can ultimately lead to its abuse and derision, or be reasons for pornography, prostitution, incest, promiscuity and celibacy.

- no longer seeing penile penetration as 'it' or as the definitive 'proof' of a loving relationship. In the most intimate and private aspect of a couple's life they feel pressurized to conform and compete with 'norms' of sex, losing sight of the fact that sexuality is an important aspect of self-expression. Instead, the union between a man and a woman should be judged more by the quality of their mutual love and devotion rather than their ability to achieve penetration. This erroneous measure of love and commitment cruelly dismisses all vaginismic marriages as 'unconsummated' and therefore 'invalid', even those lasting well beyond 20 years.

- recognition that sexual problems are generally common as opposed to uncommon and that very few people may actually have a healthy attitude towards sex, sexuality and their bodies.

- the need to emphasise the powerful healing forces that exist in communication, awareness of, and respect for sexuality:
  Increased communication about vaginismus is healing since it would lead to the uncovering of other unspoken sexual issues.
  So, too is *increased awareness* since this can lead to the removal of stigma and taboo around sexual problems. *Increased respect* for sexuality will also actively discourage our propensity to ridicule and deride, making it inappropriate to snigger and mock at people who have sexual problems.

- recognition of the resistance we all have in being truly open and unsuppressed in talking about sex.

- recognising that continually suppressing the truth about painful issues such as vaginismus ultimately makes it more difficult for women to come forward and equally difficult for vaginismus to gain recognition and understanding.

- Within the last few years the sexual climate has been radically altered by the advent of AIDS. Couples (straight and gay) are now encouraged, at least at the start of a relationship, to practise non-penetrating sex. This reappraisal brings with it an understanding that making love is still making love without intercourse. Hopefully, this will enable vaginismus sufferers to feel more included in the sexual world.

Learning about sexual love from the ancient past

There was a time (as in Ancient China) when women played significant and prominent roles in the philosophy of a society; and when their position is equal to that of men, sexual practices reflect women's equality. However, when society changes from matriarchy to patriarchy, the balance in the sexual act alters radically. As our role degenerates into a subordinate one, so too does the focus on our sexual satisfaction. The notion that psychological health is connected to one's ability to relate intimately is not new and Taoist masters pre-date Freud by many thousands of years. 'Tao' is the Chinese word for 'path' or 'way' and is the Chinese system of religion and philosophy which looks at life and its relation to eternal truth. Current Western attitudes towards sex, including its derision and pornography, are distinctly opposed to Oriental teachings. The Tao art of loving has three basic principles, and these were the ones put forward and accepted in the West mainly through the work of Masters and Johnson and the Women's Liberation Movement.[5] They are:-

– that female satisfaction is crucial

– that ejaculation be regulated and delayed

– understanding that male orgasm and ejaculation are not one and the same thing

At one time or another many of us may suffer from temporary impotence. However, the ancient Chinese never saw this as an important problem, unlike the West. Here, the words 'impotent' and 'frigid' are often over-used, misused and pejorative. The Taoists believe a man can still enter a woman by the 'soft entry' method, penetrating without an erection and using his fingers to guide him. Once inside, there is a good chance he can become erect. Soft entry shatters two myths about male sexuality:

- that a man can't enter unless he's achieved an erection
- that the erection must be very strong in order to penetrate

Soft entry may also remove the pressure from anyone who is experiencing difficulty achieving penetration.

Many practitioners stress that sufferers should be encouraged to seek help earlier so that we don't carry the shame and vaginismus around for years. If the pressure was removed from penetration and 'impotence', it would help the stigma of vaginismus to disappear, enabling us to seek help without derision or shame.

Whilst openness about sex is important, the quality of the content may be more critical than the quantity. Because there appears to be freedom in the media to discuss intimate issues, this may sometimes lull us into a false sense of openness:

> What's discussed about sexuality doesn't go far enough, so it's assumed people have trivial problems. This means discussions about sex need to be about trying to understand the experience from the sufferer's point of view
> (Susie Orbach, Psychotherapist)

Sex education for children and adults

A healthy and wholesome attitude towards sex should ideally be encouraged early, starting with the education of children. Because pornography is a source of mis information, we need to recognise that re-education may be necessary for us all and that sex education will have to do remedial work. As well as being informed about sex, children need to hear it is not only good and welcome, but that it also involves some decision making.

> We need to highlight both the pleasure of sex and the responsibility it carries
> (Dr Paul Brown, Consulting Clinical Psychologist)

Joint support from family and society

A healthier sexual climate doesn't just benefit children but would also encourage adults to discuss taboo conditions such as vaginismus and not perpetuate their concealment or the myth that vaginismus is rare. Without the shame, secrecy and fear of ridicule, a sufferer would feel less traumatized and 'unnatural'. If vaginismus became more acknowledged and understood we wouldn't have to suffer in silence but be able to seek support, not only from professionals but also from our much-needed family and friends. The enormous pressures that are sometimes insensitively placed upon a woman who hasn't yet made her mother a granny may often increase her pain and despair:

> Women don't normally go to their families and say they have vaginismus, and it's sad because spasm is not deliberate . . . parents need to understand their daughter is a normal person
> (Barbara Lamb, Nurse Psychosexual Counsellor)

Speaking out against violence and sexual abuse

Evidence exists to support the belief that vaginismus may develop following child sexual abuse and rape. It therefore follows that the safer the environment, the less incidence there will be of vaginismus. Responsibility falls upon all of us to both help the abused and treat the offender since sexual violence is often committed by people who were themselves abused:

> I go into prisons and talk about vaginismus with rapists. I explain that their crime isn't something written on a page . . . what they've actually given a woman is an inability to make love. I tell them how when I was raped I had this 'block' and couldn't be penetrated, and one of the rapists identified with this . . . something in him seemed to click
> (Jan)

It may also be that a woman who is being physically abused by her partner is not able to tell him she suffers from vaginismus. It is therefore very important that men understand exactly what vaginismus is, ending the suppression that currently exists.

THE DOCTOR'S ROLE

Because the majority of us will receive treatment from a member of the medical profession, the importance of the doctor's role in resolving vaginismus should not be under- estimated.

Creating a positive attitude towards sex and childbirth

More open attitudes towards sex would undoubtedly benefit doctors as well as the rest of us, since they are exposed to the same sexual influences in society as everyone else. Less repressed, less judgmental attitudes would create an opening for doctors to explore, understand and accept their own anxieties around intimacy. This might then encourage a less fearful atmosphere when treating vaginismus.

Many women, midwives and obstetricians stress the importance of an enjoyable and natural birth experience for mothers and babies, believing that childbirth should be less medicalized, giving more power, choice and emotional support to the labouring woman. As we learned in Chapter Three, the mother-daughter relationship is a crucial one in the developing psychology of an infant. Post-natal studies confirm that labours which are enjoyable and less frightening can increase a mother's self-esteem enabling her to feel more secure and confident in her new role of motherhood. Such positive feelings are likely to be transmitted to an infant daughter, helping to give the baby a sense of her body's future power and creativity, rather than fear, passivity and negativity.

Putting sex on the curriculum for medical students

The medical community also has a professional responsibility for ensuring that future generations of doctors are well informed about vaginismus. One way would be to introduce Human Sexuality programmes as an essential part of the curriculum in medical schools.

For example students could be taught how to notice vaginismus early on, rather than leaving it to be discovered in an ante-natal or labour ward, or in older women when the resultant treatment may be more difficult and protracted. If a doctor's training leaves him ill-prepared to recognise vaginismus, he may mistakenly diagnose an intact hymen or simply give treatment for a non-existent local infection. Even worse, he may dismiss the woman's anguish with the reassurance that 'it will right itself in the end'. As I have already explained, one well-intentioned doctor told me to 'go away and get drunk' before attempting intercourse. The more medical students are supported in trying to understand themselves, the more they are likely to be able to identify and work with their future patients' sexual problems.

Psychosexual training for General Practitioners

As explained in the previous Chapter, the primary care (GP) setting is the best place to deal with vaginismus. It is very difficult and takes a lot of courage for many of seek help and our first contact is likely to be our GP, so it would be so much better if he was psychosexually trained. Unfortunately, the reality is that there is no mandatory post-graduate training for GPs in treating vaginismus. As this training is not funded by the DHSS, doctors are required to pay for it themselves. This means taking time out from their practices and paying for a locum, which is a very expensive and time-consuming business. Surely, then, more financial assistance should be given to those general practitioners who wish to take the initiative and train.

The notion that vaginismus and the sufferer are so difficult to treat that it requires a non-GP with special training may reinforce the idea that we are somehow more 'tricky' and demanding than other patients. We are not. It has also been pointed out that for a GP to respond with 'Ah yes . . . I know an excellent expert for you', even if he does, may merely increase our sense of abnormality.[6] All that may be required of doctors to treat some women with vaginismus are increased awareness, empathy, patience and persistence.

Encouraging sensitive medical skills

As we know, in some instances it may not be the woman's general practitioner who is her first contact. It is therefore important that greater focus is placed on sensitivity for *all* doctors. Vaginismus might make a doctor feel powerless because it is preventing him from being able to examine a woman, but with appropriate guidance he could be helped to understand that she is not consciously resisting examination. It is also important that whilst the woman's fears and feelings about being examined may seem totally irrational to the doctor, he should nevertheless accept that for the woman in front of him they are real and need to be acknowledged.

Sadly, some doctors meeting vaginismus (due to their own suppressed sexual conflicts, or inadequate training?) unconsciously project their frustration and exasperation on to women presenting with spasm. My experiences match those of others whose vaginismus was received by some with impatience and intolerance instead of empathy and understanding. This may often make the therapeutic relationship unnecessarily painful.

> The doctors get cross because it makes them feel they're not very good. They are defeated by women who have vaginismus and often can't cope with their anger
> (Dr Katharine Draper, Member Inst. Psychosexual Medicine)

Although both involved in treating vaginismus, doctors and psychotherapists come from very different backgrounds. It is the nature of psychotherapy that the therapist explores and understands his own conflicts regarding a condition, whereas doctors tend to remain detached and are not encouraged to examine their own feelings. Women who suffer from vaginismus and anorexia nervosa, because of the unconscious fears of practitioners, may often be 'silenced', either by insisting on treating the symptoms inappropriately or by shouting at the woman in frustration.

Practitioners need to try and put themselves into the

woman's skin and feel her terror, despair, shame and humiliation that a symptom induces. Doctors often aren't very good at doing this, they aren't trained to deal with the distress they encounter. As a result they may distance themselves from the patient
(Susie Orbach, Psychotherapist)

We all need to be particularly careful to avoid making an assumption that all women have had sexual intercourse. This is particularly true of doctors working in VD clinics. The automatic assumption that a married or older woman is not a virgin might lead to vaginal examinations being carried out in a less gentle and sensitive manner. As explained, traumatic internals may compound vaginismus even further.

The Doctor-Nurse team

In *Louise's Treatment* we saw how nurses as well as doctors may have a valuable role to play in treating vaginismus. Unfortunately, because of financial cutbacks in the health service, very few nurses are currently being trained in psychosexual counselling and one nurse expressed to me her deep regret about this.

In Sweden, family planning is taken care of by midwives and that is why many are involved in treating vaginismus. Marianne Granö explains the advantages of this:

In our clinic, as with many other family planning clinics in Sweden, we mostly work with midwives. Doctors and midwives working closely with sexual counsellors have more experience and a more personal way of handling a difficult vaginal examination
(Marianne Granö, Sexual Psychotherapist, Sweden)

Awareness, sensitivity and collaboration are perhaps the ways forward in improving the treatment of vaginismus. Marianne Granö feels that psychotherapists and gynaecologists are too far apart:

We need to work closer with the gynaecologists. We are both very much needed in treating sexual

problems, but the ideal combination is to work together in the beginning
(Marianne Granö, Sexual Psychotherapist, Sweden)

Optimistically, things are changing in the medical world and many physicians favour the whole-person approach to medicine rather than simply viewing symptoms in isolation.

One example is the British Association of Holistic Medicine, where doctors are thinking about the experience of disorder from the human perspective
(Dr Paul Brown, Consulting Clinical Psychologist)

One homoeopath I spoke with feels his branch of medicine can and should play a much larger role in the treatment of vaginismus. He explained that many general practitioners refer patients to him if they are not responding to conventional medication:

Alternative medicine should definitely be given consideration if a woman with vaginismus hasn't had success with other treatments
(Dr. Kenneth Metson, Homoeopath)

Because vaginismus should ideally be seen as a symptom reflecting a woman's whole being, it is hoped that all practitioners (medical and non-medical) will look upon treating vaginismus within a holistic framework and with minimum physical intervention. This kind of approach would give us back our power to:
– take back self-responsibility for our health

– be questioning

– be seen as the experts on our own bodies

– be autonomous and able to fulfill our creative potential.

Accepting the realities of people and the world

No matter how sensitive and aware we all may try to be, and however skilled and kind the medical professions are, we must realistically accept that however much we try to plan for a perfect future the realities often fail to meet such

Utopian expectations. Part of human experience is that we inevitably fail in certain areas; we may lack empathy for others; we may inadvertently hurt those we love. There needs to be humility in recognising our confusion and admitting that 'Yes – maybe there are better ways of dealing with problems which we don't yet know about', and 'Yes – we have still so much to learn'.

If we can maintain a vision to be as loving, aware and sensitive as possible, and be able to acknowledge when we are not, then surely this can make a valuable contribution to increasing understanding of, giving support to, and ultimately reducing the potential for vaginismus, and all problems, occurring.

CHAPTER SEVEN

Free! To Allow in Love, Trust and Dependency

The courageous journey that a woman takes in confronting, understanding and resolving vaginismus may often be a mixture of confusion, hate, despair, pain, fear, relief and love. Similarly, the journey through this book may have re-evoked some of these emotions. In this final chapter I, along with others, describe what resolution means for us. For some it is the arrival at belonging to themselves; others, the choice and freedom to express themselves sexually. In fairytale endings people always live 'Happily Ever After', but in reality I prefer to see resolution of a problem more in terms of a strengthening process than an end in itself. Knowing there may always be obstacles to overcome and the possibility that we are able to resolve them is far more empowering than believing there is only happiness when there are no problems.

Resolution as an ongoing process

A chapter on resolution would not have been complete without acknowledging the women who, for a variety of reasons, have been unable to resolve vaginismus. The inclusion of sufferers who haven't yet reached resolution is a way of saying they too can be part of transformation and success. It may be that the experiences shared in this book will lead them on to seeking help and support. In time I hope it will become easier for us to come forward and share our pain, and for vaginismus to be responded to more imaginatively and sensitively:

  − So here I am ... middle aged ... having an awful menopause, longing for lots of sex but unable to do anything about it

- My husband has stuck by me, and we are happy in our own way. Everyone has something to contend with, and this is our cross

- I felt so humiliated when I last sought help that I will never seek it again. I try to forget about it . . . it's difficult but you get used to it as time goes on

- Actually, I haven't entirely given up hope . . . maybe there's a cure somewhere . . . I'd like to know of alternatives . . . what's worked for other people?

- I'm not bitter, just very sad at what we've had to miss all our married lives

- I still haven't given up. Always is the hope that something will work . . . someone can hypnotize me out of my fear . . . or they'll be a magic pill . . . I keep hoping for a miracle

- I've given up this year . . . hope at last has gone . . . I'll never be better and will have to face it . . .

I would therefore like to say to these women, or any one who has yet to receive appropriate help, don't ever give up . . . even if you haven't found the right help, persevere. You have a right to be free, to be your own person, and to have control over your own body.

Resolution of spasm

For doctors and therapists, transformation may be more easily defined. Most, for example, remark on how different women look after they no longer suffer from vaginismus:

> She walks in with a smile on her face and a pride in herself because she knows she's the only person who's actually made this happen
> (Dr Robina Thexton, Member Inst. Psychosexual Medicine)

One nurse-therapist says she can tell the moment a woman walks into the clinic that she has resolved her vaginismus:

The relief on her face is quite wonderful
(Barbara Lamb, Nurse Psychosexual Counsellor)

Dr Brown describes transformation within a romantic setting and likens a woman's resolution to her 'falling in love all over again'.

Another therapist said that normally he doesn't talk about 'cure' when treating sexual problems, but adds:

> Vaginismus is one of the few conditions where there is a qualitative change
> (Dr Martin Cole, Sex Therapist)

However, not all therapists see resolution in such clearly defined terms:

> It's a process more than a transformation, and the progress can go up and down
> (Marianne Granö, Sexual Psychotherapist, Sweden)

and:

> The actual spotlight on the vaginismus goes, and shifts from the vagina to the whole of the personality where the woman moves into a more indepth way of looking at herself and her inner world
> (Jill Curtis, Psychotherapist)

So what is resolution?

I accept that the ways in which I see resolution may not be acknowledged on a general level or by practitioners who may be looking more for the disappearanc of spasm. However, my vaginismus became less of a total block as I noticed other areas in my life opening up. For me, transformation didn't necessarily take place at the point when I no longer suffered from vaginismus but rather when I saw healing my spasm as a process and less of an unattainable goal to achieve. The key to resolution is in this process itself, i.e. understanding the reasons for and the ways in which we develop vaginismus. This shift of emphasis is more likely to take place if:

– vaginismus is re-situated/re-located in the areas of

love, dependency, intimacy and trust as opposed to a
woman's sexuality.

- the focus on penetration is removed to allow space for
  us to engage in exploring the deeper underlying
  causes. Continually seeing vaginismus as a sexual
  rather than emotional problem not only pressurizes us
  into seeking therapies which may be inappropriate or
  ignore one's unconscious, but also perpetuates the
  descriptions of a woman and her partner, freezing us
  into a time warp.

- resolution of vaginismus is not deemed simply when
  the symptom is alleviated, but rather when body and
  mind are in harmony.

Removing the focus from sex to the emotions may also
create the space to discuss wider issues surrounding
vaginismus, relating to other emotional blocks. For
example, one friend said that learning about vaginismus
has made her wonder just how many women suffer from
psychological vaginismus. That is, a woman who can allow
her lover to penetrate her vagina but not her heart, soul or
mind.

Goals becoming blocks

My idealisation of the act of penetration took on such
enormous proportions that I became unable to let go and
allow growth, change and love inside. In effect, my goal
became part of my unconscious closedness. If resolution is
deemed only when we no longer have spasm, then the
periods when we feel closed, depressed or have slight
difficulty with lovemaking might seem enormous failures
or steps back. If a therapy is too goal-oriented it may make
us feel desperate and hopeless that unless we reach *the*
cause we won't reach resolution. As we've seen, there is
never just one cause of vaginismus, therefore such goals
may perpetuate our hopelessness about achieving success
if they are specific and too narrowly defined. A treatment
which seeks to remove the focus from the vagina can
enable us to refrain from constantly measuring success in

terms of penetration or self-examination. Whenever I attempted to examine myself forcefully, my analyst interpreted this as an attack on both myself and the progress of therapy. I was also helped to recognise that constantly focusing on my inability to have sex somehow kept my vaginismus even more in place.

However, goals are not unimportant. The point is, they should not become blocks in resolving vaginismus. It may be more helpful if goals are ones which can be achieved today rather than tomorrow. For example, a constant aim of mine was to have a baby. When I understood that this longing also represents my need to feel and give loving feelings, I made my goal that of being able to feel and give love in the present. The goal of having a baby no longer seemed such a huge and unattainable achievement at a time when penetration was not yet possible.

Changing our conversation to re-define vaginismus

It can be both powerful and healing to change the conversation and dialogue we engage in about our problems. Though this may seem too subtle a thing to be effective, I noticed that changing the way I spoke about vaginismus also produced a shift in the way I felt. For example, when I first began writing I planned to call this book *Women Who Can't Make Love*. Then, as I started to feel free from spasm on levels other than the vaginal I saw that in continuing to say 'I can't make love' I was actually having the same conversation about vaginismus that I despised and accused others of having (that is, defining sexual ability purely in terms of penetration). It seemed hypocritical of me to expect others to view vaginismus in a more enlightened way if I wasn't prepared to, so I abandoned the use of judgmental language. I was then able to acknowledge that although I couldn't engage in penetration I was certainly able to be loving. Consequently, changing my dialogue led me to change the title of this book.

Changing our attitude can also extend to the way we define vaginismus in relation to our selves.[1] I felt deeply ashamed about my condition and discovered that I'm not alone in these feelings. We only have to think of Valerie who feels she would have to emigrate if anyone finds out she has vaginismus. If I am defined by myself and others solely as 'someone with vaginal spasm' and this has negative connotations, then it's hard for this part of myself not to seem ugly, repulsive and overwhelming. We need to be helped to move beyond this limited definition and begin to see that vaginal spasm has nothing to do with our beauty, creativity, or ability to care and love, and to see that we possess additional qualities besides spasm. Eventually, vaginismus will not automatically trigger responses of repulsion or shame but instead may be seen as just one part of the whole of a woman, not the singular most defining characteristic.[2] I am more than my vaginismus. True, spasm represents the angry, hurt, unloved parts of myself, but it is not the total Linda. No woman should ever feel she has to emotionally emigrate for shame of who she is because she is a whole person, and not just the vaginismus.

Sharing as part of solutions

Resolution of vaginismus may take very different forms. For me, part of it has been in writing this book; another, the sharing of myself with others. As time passed and my ego grew stronger it became easier and less of an ordeal to tell each progressive person. The greatest discovery was the transformation this produced in my relationships with others and theirs with me. Perhaps because I've spent so long struggling with my sexuality and the anguish that vaginismus has brought to my life, I feel a particular sensitivity towards other people's pain. Sometimes this may take the form of awareness that something painful is going on for a person without my knowing exactly what the problem is. For example, one friend tearfully confided how she and her partner had not been able to make love for more than two years. After her disclosure she apologised, saying she didn't know why she'd told me but instinctively 'knew' I'd understand. I then told her about my vaginismus. For so long the isolation and secrecy of my condition had made me feel as though I was the only woman experiencing problematic or no sex. It helped me to see that other women's sexuality may also be a painful issue and that it isn't shameful to have a sexual problem. It's only when there is less suppression that honesty about one's difficulties can emerge.

Other women feel envious and excluded, too

For the woman who succeeds in overcoming vaginismus there may be affirmation of her femininity and womanhood as well as a sense of inclusion in areas from which she had previously felt excluded. However, in sharing mutual experiences, friends admitted having similar feelings of exclusion and envy regarding sex, couples and pregnancy. A recently-divorced friend admitted it was unbearable being in the presence of couples or even hearing about weddings; another revealed how the recent announcement of a friend's pregnancy had made her feel envious and excluded, as I had so often felt. Neither of these women suffer from vaginismus, yet both had experienced similar emotions to mine. This was a revelation to me. For as long as I could remember I had harboured guilt and remorse because of my feelings on the very same issues.

I realised that feelings of envy and exclusion are neither unique nor specific to me, nor some kind of sinister pathology belonging only to a woman with vaginismus. They are part of universal human experience. Through analysis I learned that the same emotionally-charged events (pregnancy, exclusivity of couples in relationships) may trigger off primitive feelings in women who don't have vaginismus, and that such emotions originate in infancy.

Pride, relief and freedom

With the relief from longstanding feelings of shame and secrecy comes freedom to decide upon whether or not to become a mother. The rewards may be almost as great for the doctor as for the woman who has at last been able to reach this step:

> Women thank me and send me cards announcing the births of their babies

(Dr Robina Thexton, Member Inst. Psychosexual Medicine)

However, it isn't just the ability to become a mother which marks happiness and freedom. For some, motherhood is not a desire and for others it is sadly not possible. The most important factor is being able to make contact with a new self:

> I feel proud of myself that I've done something about my vaginismus . . . I feel an enormous relief because the secrecy has gone
> (Sarah)

and:

> I'm a success story . . . I'm glad I took the help that was available
> (Debbie)

CHAPTER EIGHT

Linda – Conclusion

I end where I began, by saying I feel more open and more in touch with who I am. Like us all, I have my ups and downs, but on the whole feel happier and more hopeful about the future. The desperation, alienation and isolation which so haunted me has become much less. My ability to look at and understand myself has also helped me to see my husband, family and friends more clearly. In particular, I view my parents in a different, more objective way, which has led to an understanding and acceptance of who they are, and why they act and feel as they do. Above all, healing the relationship with them has been the most powerful part of the reparative process.

I feel that I have come a long way since that toddler who screamed when sand touched her bare feet. I don't mean in actual years, but in terms of real growth. My defences against love and dependency, and my attempts to hide my needs, are now in the open . . . I feel these are the final issues for me to understand and work through.

Whilst I have always felt able to express and experience love for others, it is only now that I'm beginning to feel love for myself . . . enough at last to understand and heal my vaginismus. But the end of my story is really just the beginning, because the journey to become myself in a free and autonomous way still goes on . . .

REFERENCES:

Introduction
1 Interview between author and Dr Patricia Gillan, Consultant Psychologist, on 16th September 1987 in London.

Chapter Two: What is Vaginismus?
1 'Dyspareunia: Aspects of Painful Coitus'. Eds. H. Musaph & A.A. Haspels. 1977. Pub. by Bohn, Scheltema & Holkema, Utrecht. (P.18)
2 'The Diagnosis & Treatment of Psychosomatic Vulvovaginitis' by Joan Woodward, Psychiatric Social Worker, Brook Advisory Centre, Birmingham. From 'The Practitioner' 1981. This report describes how vaginitis may be sustained by psychological factors, and how it is not uncommon for General Practitioners to doubt that such symptoms could be psychosomatic. The suggested treatments for psychosomatic vulvovaginitis are similar to those for vaginismus.
3 'Vaginism: A Womens Problem?' by Dr Willeke Bezemer, Netherlands, for Symposium Rutgers Foundation, Heidelberg, Germany, 1987.
4 'Dyspareunia: Aspects of Painful Coitus'. Eds. H. Musaph & A.A. Haspels. 1977. Pub. by Bohn, Scheltema & Holkema, Utrecht. (P.66)
5 'Studies in the Psychology of Sex Vol.3.' by Havelock Ellis, Random House. 1900.
6 'The Psychoanalytical Dialogue of the Letters of Sigmund Freud & Karl Abraham 1907–1926'. Eds. Hilda C. Abraham & L. Freud. Pub. by Hogarth Press. 1965.
7 'Virgin Wives: A Study of Unconsummated Marriages' by Dr L.J. Friedman. 1962. Pub. Tavistock Publications Ltd. (p.37)
8 'Talking to a Stranger' by Lindsay Knight. 1986. Pub. Fontana/Collins. (p.261).
9 'Principles & Practice of Sex Therapy' by S.R. Leiblum & L.A. Pervin. 1980. Pub. Tavistock Publications Ltd. (p.191)
10 This data was gratefully researched from the computer of Dr Leonard Friedman in Massachusetts U.S.A. in August 1987.
11 Royal College of General Practitioners, 1981–1982.
12 ibid.,
13 ibid.,
14 'Primary Vaginismus: Part 1. Social & Clinical Features' by J. Barnes. Irish Medical Journal. March 1986. 79(3). (pp.59–62)
15 Royal College of Obstetricians & Gynaecologists 1975. Dr M. Duddle.
16 'Sun Newspaper': source courtesy of Deidre Sanders.
17 'Virgin Wives: A Study of Unconsummated Marriages' by Dr L.J. Friedman. 1962. Pub. Tavistock Publications Ltd. (p.130)
18 'Principles & Practice of Sex Therapy' by S.R. Leiblum & L.A. Pervin. 1980. Pub. Tavistock Publications Ltd. (p.168)
19 'Human Sexual Inadequacy' by W.H. Masters & V.E. Johnson. Pub. Bantam Books. 1970. (p.243)
20 ibid., (p.245)

21 'The New Sex Therapy' by Helen Singer Kaplan. Pub. Pelican Books. 1974. (p.460)

22 'Principles & Practice of Sex Therapy' by S.R. Leiblum & L.A. Pervin. 1980. Pub. Tavistock Publications Ltd. (pp. 181–2)

23 'Practice of Psychosexual Medicine' ED. K. Draper. Pub. John Libbey London. 1982. (p.200)

24 Extract from Ampthill Peerage case taken from The Law Reports Appeal Cases 1977 House of Lords and reprinted by kind permission of The Incorporated Council of Law Reporting for England & Wales.

25 'Practice of Psychosexual Medicine' Ed. K. Draper. Pub. John Libbey London. 1982 (p.200)

26 'Virgin Wives: A Study of Unconsummated Marriages' by Dr L.J. Friedman. 1962. Pub. Tavistock Publications Ltd. (p.72)

27 ibid., (p.72)

28 ibid., (p.72)

29 ibid., (p.72)

30 ibid., (p.73)

Chapter Three: What Causes Vaginismus?

1 'Principles & Practice of Sex Therapy' by S.R. Leiblum & L.A. Pervin. 1980. Pub. Tavistock Publications. (pp. 148–9).

2 'Dyspareunia: Aspects of Painful Coitus' Eds. H. Musaph & A.A. Haspels. 1977. Pub. Bohn, Scheltema & Holkema, Utrecht. (P.30)

3 'Understanding Women' by Luise Eichenbaum & Susie Orbach. 1983. Pub. Penguin Books Ltd. (p.17)

4 'A Layman's Guide to Psychiatry & Psychoanalysis' by Eric Berne. 1971. Pub. Penguin Books. (p.142)

5 Note: As Eichenbaum & Orbach quote in their book 'Outside In-Inside Out' (p.113):
'Feminist psychoanalysts diverge from the Object Relations Theorists in that they acknowledge that mother is not an 'object' but also a person who is a social and psychological being. What becomes internalized from this perspective isn't then the object, but the different aspects of mother. Object Relations Theorists fail to take into account the psychology of the mother and the effect of the social position of women on that mother's psychology'.

6 'Hunger Strike' by Susie Orbach. 1987. Pub. Faber & Faber. (pp.88–89)

7 The Oedipal stage in development was coined by Sigmund Freud. Oedipus was the Greek mythological figure who unknowingly killed his father and ended up marrying his mother.

8 'Dyspareunia: Aspects of Painful Coitus' Eds. H. Musaph & A.A. Haspels. 1977. Pub. Bohn, Scheltema & Holkema, Utrecht. (p.29)

9 ibid., (p.29)

10 'The New Sex Therapy' by Helen Singer Kaplan. Pub. Pelican Books. 1974. (p.459)

11 'On Women' by Clare M. Thompson. 1964, 1971. Pub. Basic Books Inc. 10 East 53rd Street, N.Y. 10022, USA. (pp.136–7)

12 'Dyspareunia: Aspects of Painful Coitus' Eds. H. Musaph & A.A. Haspels. 1977. Pub. Bohn, Scheltema & Holkema, Utrecht. (p.31)
13 'Understanding Women' by Luise Eichenbaum & Susie Orbach. 1983. Pub. Penguin Books Ltd. (pp.78–9)
14 'Dyspareunia: Aspects of Painful Coitus: Eds. H. Musaph & A.A. Haspels. 1977. Pub. Bohn, Scheltema & Holkema, Utrecht. (p.32)
15 'Vaginismus' by Dr Prudence Tunnadine. 21st November 1975. General Practitioner Magazine.
16 'Open Heart Therapy' by Bob Mandel. 1984. Pub. Celestial Arts. P.O. Box 7327, Berkeley, Calif. 94707, USA. (pp.61–2)
17 'Dyspareunia: Aspects of Painful Coitus' Eds. H. Musaph & A.A. Haspels. 1977. Pub. Bohn, Scheltema & Holkema, Utrecht. (p.28)
18 'Human Sexual Inadequacy' by W.H. Masters & V.E. Johnson. Pub. Bantam Books. 1970. (p.245)
19 ibid., (p.245)
20 'Principles & Practice of Sex Therapy' by S.R. Leiblum & L.A. Pervin. Pub. Tavistock Publications. 1980. (p.186)
21 ibid., (P.186)
22 'Virgin Wives: A Study of Unconsummated Marriages' by Dr L.J. Friedman. 1962. Pub. Tavistock Publications. (p.134)
23 ibid., (p.129)
24 'Hunger Strike' by Susie Orbach. Pub. Faber & Faber. 1987. (p.68)
25 ibid., (p.48)
26 ibid., (p.19)
27 ibid., (p.127)
28 'Outside In-Inside Out' by Luise Eichenbaum & Susie Orbach. 1982. Pub. Pelican Books. (p.87)
29 'Vaginism: A Womens Problem?' by Dr Willeke Bezemer (Netherlands) Symposium Rutgers Foundation, Heidelberg, Germany, 1987.

Chapter Four: Seeking Help

1 'Woman's Own' Magazine. Pub. IPC Magazines Ltd copyright 1985. King's Reach Tower, Stamford Street, London SE1 9LS.
2 Correspondence with Dr Prudence Tunnadine, Scientific Director, Institute of Psychosexual Medicine, London. 22nd October 1987.

Chapter Five: The Treatments & How They Work

1 'Training GPs in Psychotherapy' by Dr. M. Balint. 1954. British Medical Journal. 1,115.
2 'Virgin Wives: A Study of Unconsummated Marriages' by Dr L.J. Friedman. 1962. Pub. Tavistock Publications. (p.138)
3 'Human Sexual Inadequacy' by W.H. Masters & V.E. Johnson. Pub. Bantam Books. 1970. (p.244)
4 ibid., (p.244)
5 'Shrinks, etc' by Thomas Kiernan. 1974. Pub. The Dial Press, Dag Hammarskjold Plaza, NY 10017, USA. (p.222)
6 'Virgin Wives: A Study of Unconsummated Marriages' by Dr L.J. Friedman. 1962. Pub. Tavistock Publications. (p.62)

7 Note: Freud's theory of psychological development and his observations about women's psychology and femininity have been commented on and reappraised by feminist psychoanalysts. As Eichenbaum & Orbach state in their book 'Outside In-Inside Out' (p.106): 'Freud's concepts were made through patriarchal spectacles, either unconscious of or unconcerned about this bias. Thus, his theories relating to women's psychosexual development suffer from a particular narrow vision.'

8 'Virgin Wives: A Study of Unconsummated Marriages' by Dr L.J. Friedman. 1962. Pub. Tavistock Publications. (p.84)

9 ibid., (p.50)

10 ibid., (p.101)

11 'Feminism & Therapy' by Joanna Ryan. The Pam Smith Memorial Lecture. Pub. by Joanna Ryan and the Polytechnic of North London, 1983.

12 'Dyspareunia: Aspects of Painful Coitus' Eds. H. Musaph & A.A. Haspels. 1977. Pub. Bohn, Scheltema & Holkema, Utrecht. (p.40)

13 ibid., (pp.39–40)

14 ibid., (p.40)

15 'Human Sexual Inadequacy' by W.H. Masters & V.E. Johnson. Pub. Bantam Books. 1970. (p.244)

16 'The New Sex Therapy' by Helen Singer Kaplan. Pub. Pelican Books. 1974. (p.486)

17 'Dyspareunia: Aspects of Painful Coitus' Eds. H. Musaph & A.A. Haspels. 1977. Pub. Bohn, Scheltema & Holkema, Utrecht. (p.40)

18 'Virgin Wives: A Study of Unconsummated Marriage' by L.J. Friedman. 1962. Pub. Tavistock Publications. (p.105)

19 ibid., (pp.33–34)

20 ibid., (pp.33–34)

21 ibid., (p.105)

22 Hospital In-Patient Enquiry Data (HIPE) for the year 1985. An annual survey based upon a 10% sample of in-patient discharges.

23 Hospital Activity Analysis, Statistics Section, North West Thames Regional Health Authority. Number of 'Vaginismus Operations' performed in this area during 1985 & 1986 was 39.

24 'NHS Sex Therapy Groups for Women' by P. Gillan, S. Golombok & P. Becker. 1980. British Journal of Sexual Medicine 7. (pp.44–47)

25 'Shrinks, etc' by Thomas Kiernan. 1974. Pub. The Dial Press, NY. (p.214)

26 'Principles & Practice of Sex Therapy' by S.R. Leiblum & L.A. Pervin. 1980. Pub. Tavistock Publications. (p.388)

27 'Vaginism: A Womens Problem?' by Dr Willeke Bezemer (Netherlands) Symposium Rutgers Foundation, Heidelberg, Germany, 1987.

28 ibid.,

Chapter Six: Can Vaginismus Be Prevented?

1 'The Maturational Processes & the Facilitating Environment' by D.W. Winnicott. 1965. Pub. by Hogarth Press. (p.51)

2 'She' Magazine Sex Survey published in February 1987.
3 'The making and breaking of affectional bonds' by John Bowlby. 1979. Pub. Tavistock Publications Ltd.
4 'What Do Women Want?' by Luise Eichenbaum & Susie Orbach. 1983. Pub. Fontana Books.
5 'The Tao of Love & Sex: The Ancient Way to Ecstasy' by Jolan Chang. 1977. Pub. Wildwood House, Gower House, Croft Rd, Aldershot GU11 3HR.
6 'Vaginismus' by Dr Prudence Tunnadine. General Practitioner Magazine. 21st November 1975.

Chapter Seven: Free! To Allow in Love, Trust & Dependency
1 'Fat Is A Feminist Issue' by Susie Orbach. 1978. Pub. Arrow Books Ltd. (p.130)
2 ibid., (p.131)

BIBLIOGRAPHY:

BALINT M. 'Training GPs in Psychotherapy' (British Med. Journal 1954).

BARNES J. 'Primary Vaginismus Part 1: Social & Clinical Features' (Irish Med. Journal, Dublin 1986).

BEZEMER, W. 'Vaginism: A Womens Problem?' (Netherlands 1987).

BOWLBY J. 'The Making & Breaking of Affectional Bonds' (Tavistock Publications 1979)

CHANG J. 'The Tao of Love & Sex' (Wildwood Hse. 1977)

DRAPER K. 'Practice of Psychosexual Medicine' (London 1982)

EICHENBAUM L. 'Understanding Women' (1983 London). 'Outside In-Inside Out' (1982 London). 'What Do Women Want?' (London 1983)

ELLIS HAVELOCK. 'Studies in the Psychology of Sex Vol.3' (1900 USA)

FRIEDMAN L. 'Virgin Wives: A Study of Unconsummated Marriages' (1962 London).

GILLAN P., GOLOMBOK S. & BECKER P. 'NHS Sex Therapy Groups for Women' (Brit. Journal of Sexual Medicine 1980 London).

JOHNSON V.E. & MASTERS W.H. 'Human Sexual Inadequacy' (1970 London).

KAPLAN H.S. 'The New Sex Therapy' (1974 London).

KIERNAN T. 'Shrinks Etc' (1974 USA)

KNIGHT L. 'Talking to a Stranger' (1986 London).

LEIBLUM S.R. & PERVIN L.A. 'Principles & Practice of Sex Therapy' (1980 London)

MANDEL B. 'Open Heart Therapy' (1984 USA)

MASTERS W.H. (see JOHNSON V.E.)

MUSAPH H. & HASPELS A.A. 'Dyspareunia: Aspects of Painful Coitus' (1977 Utrecht)

ORBACH S. (see also EICHENBAUM L.) and: 'Fat Is A Feminist Issue' (London 1978) 'Hunger Strike' (London 1986)

RYAN J. 'Feminism & Therapy' (London 1983)

THOMPSON C.M. 'On Women' (USA 1971)

TUNNADINE P. 'Vaginismus' (London 1975 GP Magazine)

WINNICOTT D.W. 'The Maturational Processes & The Facilitating Environment' (London 1965)

WOODWARD J. 'The Diagnosis & Treatment of Psychosomatic Vulvovaginitis' (Birmingham 1981).

SUGGESTED READING:

The following are a selection of books which I found particularly valuable. Though they do not specifically relate to vaginismus, there are areas in each book that may have direct relevance to women having difficulties in relating intimately:

'Psychoanalysis & Feminism' by Juliet Mitchell. Penguin Books 1974. (A reassessment of Freudian psychoanalytic theories in an attempt to understand the feminine psychology and oppression of women).

'The Mirror Within' by Anne Dickson. Quartet Books 1985. (Looks afresh at basic assumptions and myths about female sexuality. It offers practical information to guide a woman through exploration of her inner feelings and her body).

'In Our Own Hands' by Sheila Ernst & Lucy Goodison. The Women's Press 1981. (Invaluable book showing how self-help and therapy is within a woman's control. Offers comprehensive guidance on individual therapy, led-groups and self-help groups with particular emphasis on the feminist aspect)

'Talking to a Stranger' by Lindsay Knight. Fontana Books 1986. (Very comprehensive guide to all the therapies written for the consumer with clear descriptions of each different therapy available).

'Understanding Women' by Luise Eichenbaum & Susie Orbach. Penguin 1983. (New theory about women's psychology developed as the experience of two feminist psychotherapists. Illustrates case histories and centres on a radical reappraisal of the mother-daughter relationship and how it is affected by social conditioning).

'Hunger Strike' by Susie Orbach. Faber & Faber 1986. (Very sympathetic and respectful approach to the anorectic woman's plight. Offers insights on how anorexia develops and guidelines as to the best therapeutic approach, including suggestions for self-help groups. Although clearly this book is not about vaginismus it is the kind of sensitive and thoughtful study that I hope will one day be written about vaginismus by a psychotherapist).

'Open Heart Therapy' by Bob Mandel. Celestial Arts 1984. (Self-help book promoting positive attitudes and affirmations about how to rediscover the inner love we all have. A list of professional Re-Birthers is included at the book of this book).

'A Crying Game' by Janine Turner. Mainstream Publishing 1984. (True account detailing a vaginismic woman's harrowing and courageous battle to free herself from a sexually violent husband. Includes interviews with two doctors specifically asked about vaginismus. Ms. Turner was unable to get help for her spasm until many years later).

'You Can Heal Your Life' by Louise L. Hay. Hay House, USA, 1984. (Self-help manual which firmly states that if we are willing to do the mental work, almost anything can be healed. Offers practical steps for dissolving both the fears and causations of diseases and emotional problems).

'How To Survive Medical Treatment' by Stephen Fulder. Century Paperbacks 1987. (Layman's guide to self-care in hospital with guidance on alternative medicine to combat side-effects of drugs and orthodox medicine.)

I have chosen the following four books on sexuality because two are specifically written for women and the other two* were the books which helped me diagnose my own vaginismus:

* 'Treat Yourself To Sex' by Paul Brown & Carolyn Faulder. Penguin 1980. (Sympathetic and down-to-earth self-help guide with suggested exercises to help overcome sexual problems. Help is also offered for women suffering from vaginismus, though the book is not aimed at women specifically.)

* 'The Book of Love' by David Delvin. New English Library 1974. (Provides extensive information with sensitive drawings on all aspects of sexuality and sexual difficulties. Vaginismus is included though the book is not aimed solely at women.)

'Woman's Experience of Sex' by Sheila Kitzinger. Penguin 1985. (This manual includes sensitive photography and drawings and focuses on every aspect of sex from the perspective of being a girl through to womanhood. Vaginismus is included.)

'Sexual Happiness for Women' by Maurice Yaffe & Elizabeth Fenwick. Dorling Kindersley Books 1986. (Very sensitive sex manual offering charts, questionnaires and programmes to help a woman discover her own sexuality. There is a guide to self-exploration and suggestions to overcome difficulties with penetration. Although written specifically for women, I think it is the sort of book men would find immensely thought-provoking!)

INDEX